# Biochemistry of Some Foodborne Microbial Toxins

# Biochemistry of Some Foodborne Microbial Toxins

*Papers presented at*
*the Symposium on Microbial Toxins*
*held at the meeting of*
*the American Chemical Society*
*New York, September 12, 1966*

EDITED BY
*Richard I. Mateles*
AND
*Gerald N. Wogan*

 The M.I.T. Press
*Massachusetts Institute of Technology*
*Cambridge, Massachusetts, and London, England*

# PREFACE

In the late 1800's it was found that certain bacteria, when they grow in foods, produce compounds that are extremely toxic to man. In this century, other bacteria of different species have been found that may grow in foods and produce toxins causing disease in those humans who ingest such foods.

As late as 1960 it was discovered that certain molds may produce compounds toxic to poultry and other animals in feeds in which a significant growth of these fungi occurs. Since that time a number of other species of molds, possibly as many as 30, have been found that produce compounds more or less toxic to animals, and some of the animal diseases caused by ingestion of these contaminated feeds have been recognized.

The significance of mold-contaminated foods in human diets is not yet well established. However, morbidity and mortality statistical data certainly imply at least the possibility that foods contaminated with mold growth of certain specific types may be responsible for diseases or malignancies and death in humans.

Significant amounts of the grain and grass feeds for animals are moldy when the feed is removed from storage. We have no idea at present as to the effect of contaminated feeds of this kind on economic losses in agriculture. It is recognized that whereas death of animals consuming such fodder may not follow economic losses caused by decreased output of milk, loss of weight or failure to gain weight, and other undesirable manifestations may result from mold-contaminated feeds.

We have learned how to control some types of bacterial foodborne intoxications in man, and in recent years have accumulated much information concerning other bacterial diseases of this type. Although fewer than ten years have passed since the discovery that some molds produce compounds toxic to animals, the chemical composition of some of these compounds has already been determined and much other information significant to the control of mold intoxication has been garnered.

The papers delivered at the symposium of which this volume is a report are concerned with the subject of bacterial and mold foodborne intoxications of man and animals. It is only through the tireless endeavors of scientists, men like those who have contributed to this symposium, that diseases can and will be controlled. Investigators in this field should obtain a certain satisfaction from their efforts to make this world a better place in which to live.

Cambridge, Massachusetts
January, 1967

J. T. R. Nickerson

# INTRODUCTION

Gerald N. Wogan
Richard I. Mateles
Department of Nutrition and Food Science
Massachusetts Institute of Technology
Cambridge, Massachusetts

The papers contained in this volume were presented at a Symposium on Microbial Toxins, of which the editors served as co-chairmen, held in New York City on September 12, 1966, during the Annual Meeting of the American Chemical Society.

Several factors were taken into account in choosing the contributions to be published. A comprehensive coverage of all known microbial toxins was not feasible, and it was decided to restrict the topics to those organisms and toxins that pose direct problems as food contaminants or are otherwise closely related to the food supply. This general area was divided into two broad categories, bacterial and algal toxins on the one hand and fungal toxins (mycotoxins) on the other. The subject matter was further narrowed to areas of research that had not recently been reviewed extensively or to new information on problems being studied currently and actively. The result of this selection is illustrated, for example, by the inclusion of only one paper dealing with aflatoxins, which are being intensively studied and have been the subjects of many recent symposia and publications. The format of the Symposium, which is reflected in the present volume, included one session on bacterial and algal toxins and a second session on mycotoxins.

In the session on bacterial and algal toxins, M. S. Bergdoll reviewed the present knowledge of the chemistry and biochemistry of staphylococcal enterotoxins. These are the agents responsible for common food poisonings caused by contamination of foods by staphylococci.

The botulinum toxins are among the most potent protein toxins known and are responsible for the frequently fatal, but fortunately uncommon, type of food poisoning known as botulism. D. A. Boroff presented recent research carried out to characterize the type A toxin and to determine which portion of the protein molecule is responsible for its activity.

A. G. van Veen presented a comprehensive discussion of bongkrek poisoning. This is a food poisoning, common to parts of Indonesia, which is caused by growth in fermented coconut products of a pseudomonad instead of the usual and desired fungus. Relatively unknown in the West, this type of poisoning has been responsible for many deaths in Indonesia.

E. J. Schantz discussed the chemistry of various toxins produced by algae. While some of these algae are ingested by mussels and other shellfish and cause poisoning when these shellfish are later consumed by humans, other algal species are of significance because of their effect on fish raised in ponds for food purposes.

In the session on mycotoxins, A. Taylor reviewed the chemistry and biochemistry of sporidesmins and related compounds. These toxins, produced by species of Pithomyces and Chaetomium, are exceedingly potent cytotoxic agents in vitro and sporidesmin has been identified as the causative agent in facial eczema disease in ruminants in New Zealand and Australia. Toxicity syndromes apparently arise as a consequence of growth of toxin-producing molds on pasture grasses.

The furocoumarins, including a series of substitute psoralens, are strongly phototoxic compounds. Isolation of these compounds from celery infected with Sclerotinia sclerotiorum and information on structure-activity relationships were discussed by L. D. Scheel. Although the causative role of two of these compounds, 8-methoxy-psoralen and 4, 5, 8 trimethylpsoralen, in phototoxicity lesions of the skin has been established, their possible importance as diet contaminants has not yet received extensive study.

C. J. Mirocha described the isolation and chemical characterization of a strongly estrogenic metabolite of Fusarium graminearum. Growth of this fungus on corn used for animal feeds is thought to be responsible for field cases of an estrogenic syndrome of swine. The substance was shown to be a fluorescent derivative of resorcinol with a high order of potency as an estrogen.

Chemical assay methods for aflatoxin contamination of foodstuffs are based upon fluorescence and chromatographic criteria of suitably prepared extracts of the food. The specificity of these methods is compromised by the presence in the food of nonaflatoxin compounds with similar chemical properties. Production of a variety of such substances by molds used in the Japanese fermentation industries and a summary of their properties was described by T. Yokotsuka.

Systematic searches for the ability of spoilage fungi to produce toxic metabolites have recently resulted in the isolation of several previously unknown mycotoxins. Notable among these are the so-called ochratoxins isolated from cultures of Aspergillus ochraceus by a group of investigators at the CSIR Laboratories, Pretoria, South Africa. A summary of the chemical nature, experimental toxicity and microbiological aspects of production of ochratoxins was presented by W. Nel, a member of the research group. The significance of ochratoxins as food contaminants has not yet been established, as the compounds have not been detected in materials used in human or animal diets.

# CONTENTS

## PART I. BACTERIAL AND ALGAL TOXINS

## PART II. FUNGAL TOXINS

# THE STAPHYLOCOCCAL ENTEROTOXINS

Merlin S. Bergdoll
Food Research Institute
University of Wisconsin
Madison, Wisconsin

The enterotoxins are proteins produced by the staphylococci under certain conditions in foods and culture media. The ingestion of these substances by humans results in what is called staphylococcus food poisoning. This type of foodborne illness, of worldwide occurrence, is characterized by vomiting and diarrhea that occurs 2 to 5 hours after eating the contaminated food. The investigations of Dack et al. in 1930 indicated a toxic substance produced by the staphylococci to be the causative agent.

Only occasional attempts were made in the period 1930-1950 to determine the nature of the toxic agent. The workers conducting these investigations disagreed as to whether the enterotoxin was a carbohydrate or a protein (Darrach, 1941; Davison, 1940, Hammon, 1941; Minett, 1938). In 1948, a long-range investigation was undertaken at the Food Research Institute* to elucidate the properties of the enterotoxin. A number of other investigations have been undertaken in the last several years on various phases of the enterotoxin problem. More information about the enterotoxins is available than can be covered here; therefore, the main emphasis of this discussion will be on the purification and physicochemical properties of the enterotoxins, with some discussion of assay and production. Although reports are available on the identification of new enterotoxins (Bergdoll et al., 1965a; Casman et al., 1966), detection of enterotoxins in foods (Casman and Bennett, 1965; Hall et al., 1965; Read et al., 1965a; Read et al., 1965b), and the mechanism of action of the enterotoxins in the food poisoning syndrome (Sugiyama, 1966), no attempt will be made to review these areas.

In the preliminary investigations at the Food Research Institute it was assumed that the causative agent of staphylococcus intoxica-

---

*Associated with the University of Chicago until 1966, and since then with the University of Wisconsin.

tion was a single substance.  Only after the purification of a protein responsible for illness induced in monkeys was the existence
of more than one enterotoxin discovered.  The basis for differentiation of the enterotoxins is their reaction with specific antibodies.  In 1962 (Casman et al., 1963) this method of identification was used to establish a nomenclature for the enterotoxins,
designating them enterotoxins A, B, C, etc.  To date, three
enterotoxins have been definitely identified (Bergdoll et al., 1959b;
Bergdoll et al., 1965a; Casman, 1960) and a fourth tentatively
identified (Casman et al., 1966).  All of the enterotoxins discovered so far have been implicated in food poisoning outbreaks;
however, enterotoxin A is the one most frequently identified with
food poisoning.  Enterotoxin B, although occasionally involved in
food poisoning, has been associated most frequently with staphylococcus strains isolated in connection with other human ailments
such as enteritis.  Surgalla and Dack (1955) reported that of 32
strains isolated from patients suffering with enteritis 30 produced
enterotoxin, and 26 of these produced enterotoxin B.  Enterotoxin
C is produced by a number of strains isolated from foods implicated
in food poisoning outbreaks (Bergdoll et al., 1965a).  Enterotoxin D
is associated with strains implicated in food poisoning; however,
many of these strains also produce enterotoxins A, B, or C (Casman
et al., 1966).  Another enterotoxin (or enterotoxins) has not been
associated with a specific antibody.

In the course of the investigations in the Food Research Institute
laboratories, two enterotoxin C's (from separate Staphylococcus
aureus strains) were purified.  Although they appear to be identical
in most respects, their movements in an electrical field are quite
different.  Enterotoxin C (strain 137) has an isoelectric point at
pH 8.6, and enterotoxin C (strain 361) has an isoelectric point at
pH 7.0.  For the purposes of this discussion, enterotoxin C (strain
137) will be referred to as $C_1$, and enterotoxin C (strain 361) will
be referred to as $C_2$.

## Determination of the Enterotoxins

A major problem confronting investigators in the enterotoxin
field is the lack of a practical quantitative assay.  Several species
of animals, including monkeys (Jordan and McBroom, 1931;
Surgalla et al., 1953), cats (Dolman et al., 1936; Hammon, 1941),
dogs (Dolman et al., 1936; J. L. Fowler, personal communication; Nikodemusz et al., 1962; Sugiyama et al., 1960), pigs
(Hopkins and Poland, 1942), pigeons (H. Lineweaver, personal
communication), and frogs (Eddy, 1951; Robinton, 1950), have
been used to determine the biological activity of the enterotoxins.
Animals other than the monkey are relatively insensitive to the
enterotoxins unless they are injected intraperitoneally or intravenously.  Because emesis is the most readily observable reac-

tion to enterotoxin, animals having no vomiting mechanism, e.g., rodents, have been of little use as test animals.

The methods most frequently employed are intraperitoneal or intravenous injections of cats and kittens (Dolman et al., 1936; Hammon, 1941), and feeding of young rhesus monkeys (Surgalla et al., 1953). The cat method requires the inactivation of substances that may provoke symptoms similar to those caused by enterotoxin when administered by parenteral routes. Heating at 100°C for 20 to 30 minutes (Davison et al., 1938; Dolman et al., 1936), treatment with trypsin (Denny and Bohrer, 1963), and use of antisera (Dolman, 1943) to inactivate the interfering substances have been used with success. One cannot be sure, however, that these methods inactivate all interfering substances in every instance. Another disadvantage in using the cat method is that cats are relatively insensitive to enterotoxin C. Approximately 50 times more enterotoxin C than enterotoxins A or B is required to produce emesis in cats (Casman et al., 1966).

The most reliable bioassay for the enterotoxins is the feeding of young rhesus monkeys. Of the toxic moities produced by the staphylococci, only the enterotoxins cause emesis in these animals. Assays are made by administering the enterotoxins in solution (usually 50 ml) to young monkeys (2 to 3 kg) by catheter (Surgalla et al., 1953). The animals are observed for five hours after feeding; vomiting is accepted as positive reaction for enterotoxin. To determine the presence of enterotoxin in a given sample, six monkeys are used and emesis in at least two animals in considered a positive reaction. To determine the approximate potency of the purified enterotoxins, six or more monkeys are fed at three or more twofold levels of the purified enterotoxin (Table 1). Because monkeys rapidly develop resistance to enterotoxin, those previously exposed to not more than one enterotoxin feeding are used for the latter experiments. The original cost of monkeys and the expense of their upkeep limit the number of animals that can be maintained.

Because the enterotoxins are antigenic, assay techniques based on the antigen-antibody reaction were developed. The antigen-antibody reaction may not necessarily indicate biological activity; however, in most instances, correlation between the two is adequate to justify using the immunological reaction in assaying for enterotoxin.

Hemagglutination inhibition (Robinson and Thatcher, 1965; Morse and Mah, personal communication), immunofluorescence (Friedman and White, 1965; Genigeorgis and Sadler, 1966), rhodamine-labeled antibodies (Hopper, 1963), and various techniques employing gel diffusion have been investigated. Modifications of the following methods involving gel diffusion have been reported: the Ouchterlony plate (Bergdoll et al., 1959b; Bergdoll et al., 1965a; Casman, 1960), the Wadsworth microslide (Casman and Bennett, 1963; Hall

Table 1.   Effect of Enterotoxin A on Rhesus Monkeys*

Route of Administration

| Intragastric | | Intravenous | |
|---|---|---|---|
| Amount μg/animal | Result† | Amount μg/kg | Result† |
| 5 | 4/10 | 0.017 | 2/6 |
| 10 | 16/30 | 0.035 | 2/9 |
| 20 | 9/12 | 0.070 | 4/9 |
| | | 0.140 | 5/6 |

*Chu et al., 1966.
†Number vomiting versus number challenged.

et al., 1965), the comparator cell (Bergdoll et al., 1959b; Surgalla et al., 1952), the Oakley double-diffusion tube (Bergdoll et al., 1959a; Bergdoll et al., 1961; Hall et al., 1965), and the Oudin single gel-diffusion tube methods (Bergdoll et al., 1959a; Surgalla et al., 1952). These methods are used qualitatively for the detection of the enterotoxins, with the exception of the single diffusion tube method that has been adapted for their quantitative determination (Bergdoll, 1962; Hall et al., 1963; Read et al., 1965a; Weirether et al., 1966).

In the single-diffusion tube method, an agar column (4 mm diameter) containing the enterotoxin antiserum is layered with the enterotoxin solution (5 to 200 μg/ml). The front of the enterotoxin-anti-enterotoxin precipitin band that is formed in the antiserum-agar column moves down the column at a rate corresponding to the concentration of the enterotoxin and the concentration of the antibody. The distance that the band moves in a given time is measured, and the enterotoxin concentration is calculated from a standard curve (Figure 1). The standard curve is obtained by plotting the log of known enterotoxin concentrations (μg/ml) against the distance that the enterotoxin-antienterotoxin band moves in mm into the agar column in a given time. Incubation for seven days at 25°C is the standard procedure at the Food Research Institute; however, other investigators incubate for shorter periods of time at higher temperatures (Hall et al., 1963; Read et al., 1965a; Weirether et al., 1966). Because the movement of the precipitin band is affected by pH and salt concentration, the enterotoxin samples to be analyzed are either dialyzed against the standard gel-duffusion buffer (0.02 M phosphate buffer, $Na_2HPO_4$-$KH_2PO_4$, pH 7.4 containing 0.85% NaCl and 1:10,000 merthiolate), or the enterotoxin used in obtaining the standard curve is dissolved in the solution employed in the experiments (Table 2) (Kato et al., 1966).

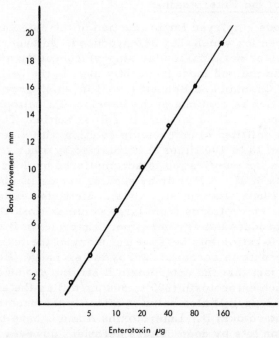

Fig. 1. Standard curve for determination of enterotoxin B. Standard antigen: enterotoxin of an estimated "95%" purity. Standard antibody: 3-fold dilution of serum obtained from rabbits immunized with "70%" enterotoxin. Time of band development: 7 days. (Bergdoll, 1962.)

Table 2. Band Movements in Single Diffusion Tubes of Known Amounts of Enterotoxin A Dissolved in Varying Concentrations of PHP and NAK*

| Concentration of PHP and NAK | Enterotoxin A Concentration (µg/ml) | | | |
|---|---|---|---|---|
| | 2.5 | 5.0 | 10 | 20 |
| | Band Movement (mm)† | | | |
| 0.02 M Phosphate Buffer (Control) | 0 | 2.5 ± 0.1 | 6.0 ± 0.2 | 9.7 ± 0.1 |
| 1% Each | 3.1 ± 0.2 | 5.4 ± 0.3 | 8.9 ± 0.1 | 12.0 ± 0.3 |
| 2% Each | 4.0 ± 0.2 | 6.5 ± 0.3 | 9.0 ± 0.2 | 12.6 ± 0.2 |
| 3% Each | 4.4 ± 0.1 | 6.7 ± 0.1 | 9.5 ± 0.3 | 12.6 ± 0.2 |
| 4% Each | 3.9 ± 0.3 | 5.8 ± 0.2 | 9.2 ± 0.2 | 12.2 ± 0.2 |
| Average | 3.9 | 6.1 | 9.2 | 12.4 |

*From Kato et al., 1966.
†Figures given are averages of results from four diffusion tubes.

## Production of the Enterotoxins

The methods employed for production of the enterotoxins depend on the purpose for which they are produced. In order to determine whether or not a particular staphylococcus strain is enterotoxigenic, the method most frequently used is the cellophane sac technique of Casman and Bennett (1963) in which growth and enterotoxin production is confined to the interior of a cellophane sac lying on the surface of a fluid medium in a Roux bottle. This technique provides one milliter of enterotoxin solution with an enterotoxin concentration 20 to 100 times that obtained by other methods.

Production for purification is accomplished by deep culture aeration (Surgalla et al., 1951) or by shaking during incubation (Bergdoll et al., 1965a; Kato et al., 1966). Methods available for recovery of the enterotoxins from large volumes limit the quantities that can be produced at any one time. Enterotoxin B can be produced in 1000-gallon lots because recovery of the toxin from the culture supernate is accomplished by ion exchange (Bergdoll et al., 1961). The fact that the enterotoxin B strains produce 50 to 100 times as much enterotoxin (200 to 500 $\mu$g/ml) as the enterotoxin A strains (2 to 5 $\mu$g/ml) also helps to simplify the problem of recovery of enterotoxin B. Enterotoxins A and C have been produced in 1000-gallon lots by deep culture aeration; however, the only satisfactory method for recovery of the A and C enterotoxins from these large volumes is precipitation with trichloroacetic acid (Chu et al., 1966). This method was abandoned when it appeared that the precipitated enterotoxin was readily denatured during the purification and the impurities in the precipitated material were difficult to separate from the enterotoxin. The alternate procedure of production of enterotoxins A and C in two-liter Erlenmeyer flasks (400 to 600 ml per flask) by incubation on gyrotory shakers was adopted (Kato et al., 1966). The supernate is concentrated 10- to 20-fold by dialysis against Carbowax and is either freeze-dried or used directly for purification.

Several media have been employed for the production of the enterotoxins (Casman, 1958; Casman and Bennett, 1963; Dolman, 1943; Favorite and Hammon, 1941; Kato et al., 1966; Surgalla et al., 1951). The ones most frequently utilized are pancreatic digests of casein such as Protein Hydrolysate Powder (PHP) obtained from Mead Johnson and Co. and some of the hydrolysates such as Edamin S and N-Z Amine NAK (NAK) produced by Sheffield Chemical Co. The best results for volume production of the enterotoxins have been with 3% PHP plus 3% NAK supplemented with 0.001% niacin and 0.00005% thiamin, adjusted to pH 6.0 to 7.0 and incubated on a gyrotory shaker at approximately 275 rpm for 18 to 24 hours at 37°C (Table 3).

Table 3.   The Effect of Medium on the Production of
Enterotoxin B*

| Medium† | Final pH | Optical Density | Enterotoxin‡ µg/ml |
|---|---|---|---|
| 2% PHP | 8.4 | 3.10 | 200 |
| 2% N-Z Amine A | 8.4 | 1.20 | 40 |
| 4% N-Z Amine A | 8.2 | 2.10 | 110 |
| 3% N-Z Amine A + 0.1% K₂HPO₄ | 8.3 | 2.60 | 210 |
| 1% PHP + 1% N-Z Amine A | 8.3 | 2.30 | 190 |
| 3% PHP + 3% N-Z Amine NAK | 8.2 | 9.60 | 480 |

*From Kato et al., 1966.
†Supplemented with 0.001% niacin and 0.00005% thiamin, and
adjusted to pH 6.5.   Incubation at 37°C for 18 hours on a
gyrotory shaker (280 rpm).
‡Enterotoxin determined by gel diffusion.

## Recovery of the Enterotoxins from Culture Supernates

The relatively small amounts of the enterotoxins produced in culture media by the staphlococci necessitated concentrating the enterotoxins before attempting to purify them.  This was done initially by adjustment of the culture supernates to pH 3.5 with 85% $H_3PO_4$ followed by recovery of the precipitate containing the enterotoxin by filtration through a bed of filter-aid.  The enterotoxin was subsequently recovered from the filter-aid by extraction with 0.05 M $Na_2HPO_4$ (Bergdoll et al., 1959a).  An improved method for recovery of enterotoxin B was reported in 1961 by Bergdoll et al., in which the ion-exchange resin Amberlite IRC-50 (XE-64) was used to adsorb the enterotoxin directly from the culture supernate.  This method is utilized as the initial step of the current method for purification of enterotoxin B (Schantz et al., 1965).

For recovery of enterotoxin A, the phosphoric acid precipitation technique was replaced by precipitation with trichloracetic acid at pH 2.9 (Chu et al., 1966).  More complete precipitation of the enterotoxin was possible with this method than with phosphoric acid; however, both precipitation methods appeared partially to denature the enterotoxin.  In order to circumvent the problems encountered as a result of precipitation, production was limited to volumes that could be concentrated by other means. The method currently in use in the Food Research Institute laboratories is dialysis of the supernate for 24 to 48 hours against an equal volume of 50% aqueous Carbowax 20 M (Union Carbide Corporation, New York, N. Y.) followed by dialysis against water. The dialyzed crude enterotoxin (10- to 20-fold concentration) is used for purification either before or after freeze-drying (Chu et al., 1966; Frea et al., 1963).

## Purification of the Enterotoxins

The purification studies in the Food Research Institute laboratories were undertaken with the assumption that enterotoxin was a protein. Such methods as precipitation with $(NH_4)_2SO_4$, HCl, and ethanol and methanol at subzero temperatures proved useful in its recovery and partial purification (Bergdoll et al., 1951). To obtain preparations of higher purity using other than precipitation techniques, an attempt was made to purify the enterotoxin chromatographically with diatomaceous silica (Hyflo Super Cel) (Bergdoll et al., 1952). The relatively low capacity of Hyflo Super Cel for the enterotoxin led to the use of other adsorbents such as alumina and the ion exchange resin, Amberlite IRC-50 (XE-64) (Bergdoll et al., 1959a). In addition, techniques employing electrophoresis in a supporting medium such as starch were found to be useful in obtaining an enterotoxin preparation of high purity. With the advent of carboxymethyl-cellulose (CM-cellulose) and Sephadex, purification can now be accomplished without employing the more cumbersome precipitation and starch electrophoresis techniques. Procedures for purification of the enterotoxins are outlined here. Although the general methods employed are similar, the detailed procedures are different because each was worked out by separate investigators. It is probable that the enterotoxins with similar isoelectric points, such as A and $C_2$, can be purified by the same methods; however, attempts to purify enterotoxins with different isoelectric points by the same methods may prove to be more difficult. Casman and Bennett (1964) attempted to purify enterotoxin A by modification of the procedures described by Bergdoll et al. (1959a) for purification of enterotoxin B. Comparison of their preparation and the enterotoxin A purified by Chu et al. (1966) indicated the enterotoxin A content of the Casman and Bennett preparation was approximately 25 to 30% (Kato et al., 1966) of that of the preparation of Chu et al.

Enterotoxin A. The purification of enterotoxin A has been accomplished by Chu et al. (1966) using the following procedures: (1) concentration of the culture supernate 10- to 20-fold with Carbowax 20 M followed by dialysis against deionized water; (2) adsorption on CM-cellulose (equilibrated with 0.01 M sodium phosphate at pH 5.7) and subsequent elution with 0.02 M Na₂HPO₄; (3) adsorption on CM-cellulose (equilibrated with 0.01 M sodium phosphate at pH 6.0) from the dialyzed eluate (from step 2) adjusted to pH 6.0 and subsequent elution with a gradient phosphate buffer from 0.01 M at pH 6.0 to 0.05 M at pH 6.6; (4) gel filtration of the dialyzed, lyophilized eluate (from step 3) dissolved in 5 ml of 0.05 M sodium phosphate at pH 6.8 with Sephadex G-100; (5) gel filtration of the lyophilized enterotoxin (from step 4) dissolved in 5 ml distilled water with Sephadex G-75 equilibrated and developed with 0.005 M sodium phosphate, pH 6.85; and (6) dialysis and freeze-drying  The over-all yield of purified enterotoxin A is usually 30 to 35% based on gel-diffusion tests on the original culture supernates.

Enterotoxin B.  The purification of what is now called enterotoxin B was first reported in 1959 by Bergdoll et al. (1959a). Purification was accomplished by the following procedures: (1) precipitation at pH 3.5 with H₃PO₄; (2) adsorption on alumina from 0.03 M sodium phosphate at pH 6.3 and subsequent elution with 0.2 M Na₂HPO₄; (3) precipitation from 40% ethanol at -7°C; (4) adsorption on Amberlite IRC-50 (XE-64) (equilibrated with 0.05 M sodium phosphate at pH 6.8) from 0.02 M sodium phosphate at pH 6.2 and subsequent elution with 0.05 M sodium phosphate at pH 6.8; (5) precipitation from 25% ethanol at -13°C; (6) electrophoresis in 0.05 M sodium phosphate at pH 6 with starch as the supporting medium; (7) precipitation from 30% ethanol at -13°C; and (8) freeze-drying.  This method is lengthy and not readily adaptable for preparation of large quantities of the enterotoxin. It has been modified and adapted for purification of enterotoxin B in multiple gram lots by Schantz et al. (1965) as follows: (1) adsorption on the ion exchange resin, CG-50, from the culture supernate diluted with two volumes of water and adjusted to pH 6.4, and subsequent elution with 0.5 M sodium phosphate at pH 6.8 in 0.25 M NaCl; (2) adsorption on CG-50 (equilibrated with 0.05 M sodium phosphate at pH 6.8) from the dialyzed eluate from step 1 (to reduce salts to less than 0.01 M) and subsequent elution with 0.15 M Na₂HPO₄; (3) adsorption on CM-cellulose (equilibrated with 0.01 M sodium phosphate at pH 6.2) from the dialyzed eluate from step 2 (to reduce salts to less than 0.01 M) and subsequent elution with a linear-gradient phosphate buffer from 0.02 M at pH 6.2 to 0.07 M at pH 6.8; and (4) dialysis to reduce the buffer salts to 2 to 3% of the protein concentration, centrifuged to remove any insoluble material and freeze-dried. The over-all yield of purified toxin usually amounted to 50 to 60% based on gel-diffusion tests on the original culture supernate.

The purification of enterotoxin B has also been reported by Frea et al. (1963).  In the method developed by these investiga-

tors, the enterotoxin was isolated from the bacterial culture
supernate (concentrated by dialysis against polyethylene glycol)
by the following procedures: (1) precipitation from 40% ethanol
at -15°C (enterotoxin dissolved in 0.02 M sodium phosphate, pH
6.8); (2) gel filtration of the enterotoxin precipitate (step 1) in
0.02 M sodium phosphate, pH 6.8, with Sephadex G-100; and (3)
Sephadex column electrophoresis of the dialyzed, freeze-dried
enterotoxin (step 2) in 0.015 M sodium phosphate at pH 6.0. These
investigators report that the purified enterotoxin obtained by this
method was nearly homogeneous on disc electrophoresis and
showed only one line of precipitation in gel-diffusion tests. Emesis
in monkeys resulted when the purified toxin was injected intravenously at the rate of 0.26 μg of nitrogen per kg of body weight. An
attempt was made to compare these results with those reported by
Bergdoll et al. (1959a) without noting that the results of the latter
workers were obtained by intragastric injection of the toxin. Considering that approximately ten times as much enterotoxin is required to cause emesis by the intragastric route as by the intravenous route, their preparation was actually less potent than the
one to which it was compared (Schantz et al., 1965). The methods
they used were new; however, apparently additional steps are
needed to give a high degree of purity. The gel filtration technique with Sephadex has been applied to the purification of the
other enterotoxins.

Enterotoxin $C_1$ (Staphylococcus aureus, strain 137). The purification of enterotoxin $C_1$ (Staphylococcus aureus, strain 137) has
been accomplished by Borja and Bergdoll (1967) by the following
procedures: (1) concentration of the culture supernate 10 to 20-
fold with Carbowax 20 M followed by dialysis against deionized
water and freeze-drying; (2) adsorption in CM-cellulose (equilibrated with 0.01 M sodium phosphate at pH 5.5) from 0.01 M
sodium phosphate at pH 5.5, and subsequent stepwise elution with
0.02 M sodium phosphate at pH 6.1, and 0.06 M sodium phosphate
at pH 6.6; (3) gel filtration of the freeze-dried 0.06 M sodium
phosphate at pH 6.6 eluate (step 2) in 0.02 M sodium phosphate
at pH 6.8 with Sephadex G-75; (4) gel filtration of the freeze-dried
enterotoxin fraction (step 3) in 0.02 M sodium phosphate at pH 6.8
with Sephadex G-50; (5) repeat of step 4; and (6) dialysis and
freeze-drying. The over-all yield of purified enterotoxin $C_1$ is
usually 15 to 20% based on gel-diffusion tests on the original
culture supernate.

Enterotoxin $C_2$ (Staphylococcus aureus, strain 361). The purification of enterotoxin $C_2$ (Staphylococcus aureus, strain 361) has
been accomplished by Avena and Bergdoll (1967) by the following
procedures: (1) concentration of the culture supernate 10- to 20-
fold with Carbowax 20 M followed by dialysis against deionized
water and freeze-drying; (2) adsorption on CM cellulose (equilibrated with 0.02 M sodium phosphate at pH 5.4) from 0.02 M

sodium phosphate at pH 5.4 and subsequent elution with 0.06 M
sodium phosphate at pH 6.6 to 6.7; (3) adsorption on CM-cellulose (equilibrated with 0.005 M sodium phosphate at pH 5.8 to
5.9) from 0.005 M sodium phosphate at pH 5.8 to 5.9 followed by
elution with a gradient phosphate buffer from 0.005 M at pH 5.8
to 5.9 to 0.05 M at pH 5.8 to 5.9; (4) gel filtration of the dialyzed,
freeze-dried eluate (from step 3) dissolved in 0.02 M sodium phosphate at pH 6.8 with Sephadex G-75; (5) gel filtration of the dialyzed, freeze-dried enterotoxin (from step 4) dissolved in 0.02 M
sodium phosphate at pH 6.8 with Sephadex G-50; and (6) dialysis
and freeze-drying. The over-all yield of purified enterotoxin $C_2$
is usually 35 to 40% based on gel-diffusion tests on the original
culture supernate.

## Properties of the Enterotoxins

The purified enterotoxins are fluffy, snow-white materials that
are hygroscopic and easily soluble in water and salt solutions
(Avena and Bergdoll, 1967; Bergdoll et al., 1959a; Borja and
Bergdoll, 1967; Chu et al., 1966; Schantz et al., 1965). Tests
with the purified enterotoxins for carbohydrate, lipid, nucleic
acids, $\alpha$- and $\beta$-lysins, apyrase, coagulase, fibrinolysin and
proteolytic enzymes were negative.

The biological potency of the enterotoxins as determined by administration of the toxins intragastrically or intravenously into
young rhesus monkeys (2 to 3 kg) is exemplified by the results
for enterotoxin A given in Table 1. From the tests that have been
made, all of the enterotoxins appear to be equal in potency; i.e.,
5 µg intragastrically are required to cause emesis in 50% of the
animals. The only enterotoxin that has been tested in a large
number of monkeys is enterotoxin B. Schantz et al. (1965) used
more than 200 animals for intravenous injections and about 100
animals for intragastric administration. They reported that, by
the intravenous route, illness characterized by vomiting or diarrhea was observed in 50% of the animals (effective dose, $ED_{50}$)
at 0.1 µg/kg body weight with 95% confidence limits of 0.4 to 0.9.
By the oral route, the $ED_{50}$ was 0.9 µg/kg body weight (95% confidence limits: 0.2 to 5) with a probit slope of 1.0 (95% confidence
limits of 0.2 to 2). The data were analyzed by the probit regres-
sion method suggested by Finney (1952).

Effect of heat on the enterotoxins. The biological activities of
enterotoxin B were retained after heating a solution of the toxin
at 60°C and pH 7.3 for as long as 16 hours (Schantz et al., 1965).
A decrease of 50% in the reaction of enterotoxin A with its specific antibody resulted when it was heated at pH 6.85 at 60°C for 20
minutes (Chu et al., 1966). Heating of enterotoxin $C_1$ at 60°C for
30 minutes resulted in no change in the reaction of the enterotoxin
with its specific antibody; however, after 60 minutes, the solution

became turbid (Borja and Bergdoll, 1967). Solutions of enterotoxin $C_2$ became turbid when heated at 52°C (Avena and Bergdoll, 1967). Less than 50% of the biological activity of enterotoxin B was destroyed when the toxin was heated at 100°C for 5 minutes although the toxin was coagulated at this temperature. Enterotoxin A no longer reacted with its specific antibody after heating at 80°C for 3 minutes or at 100°C for 1 minute. The reaction of enterotoxin $C_2$ with antienterotoxin was reduced to about 20% of normal when it was heated at 100°C for 1 minute. These results indicate that of the enterotoxins, A is the most sensitive to heat, while B is the least sensitive. The sensitivity of enterotoxin A to denaturation hampered the efforts to purify this enterotoxin.

For many years, it was the practice in the Food Research Institute laboratories to store purified enterotoxin B in a desiccator at room temperature. Occasionally some insolubility and loss of activity was noted after long storage periods. Schantz et al. (1965) reported that freeze-dried enterotoxin B stored (with desiccant) at 4°C for over one year showed no loss in biological activity or changes in its solubility in water, but when it was stored at room temperature for this length of time, some insolubility and loss in biological activity was observed. It is therefore recommended that the purified enterotoxins be stored under desiccation at refrigeration temperatures. Specific information is not available about storage of each of the enterotoxins in solution; however, enterotoxin A (10-20 μg/ml 0.85% saline) has been stored in the frozen state for several months without apparent loss of activity. This is a convenient method for storage of the enterotoxins when only very small amounts are required for any given experiment.

The enterotoxins in the active state are resistant to proteolytic enzymes such as trypsin, chymotrypsin, rennin, and papain. Pepsin destroys their activity at a pH of about 2, but is ineffective at higher pH values (Bergdoll, 1966; Chu et al., 1966; Schantz et al., 1965).

The nitrogen content of the enterotoxins is consistent with that of most proteins, with the possible exception of enterotoxin A. The values obtained for A with an F & M Scientific Model 185 carbon hydrogen nitrogen analyzer were consistently 0.4 to 0.5% lower than the nitrogen value calculated from the amino acid composition. After several rechecks of the amino acid composition it was concluded that the nitrogen content of this enterotoxin is 16.4 to 16.5% and that the lower values obtained by the analyzer were due to difficulties in obtaining the correct dry weight of this protein.

Some of the chemical and physical properties of the enterotoxins are given in Table 4. The sedimentation velocity measurements were made according to Schachman (1957; 1959) with a Spinco Model E analytical ultracentrifuge with either a conventional 12-mm cell with 4° sector or a rubber-valve-type, synthetic-boundary cell.

Table 4.   Some Properties of the Enterotoxins

| | Enterotoxin | | | |
|---|---|---|---|---|
| | A | B | $C_1$ | $C_2$ |
| Emetic Dose ($ED_{50}$) (Monkey) ($\mu g$/animal) | 5 | 5 | 5 | 5-10 |
| Nitrogen Content (%) | 16.5 | 16.1 | 16.2 | 16.0 |
| Sedimentation Coefficient ($s^o_{20,w}$), S | 3.04 | 2.89* 2.78† | 3.00 | 2.90 |
| Diffusion Coefficient ($D^o_{20,w}$), $\times 10^{-7}$ $cm^2$ $sec^{-1}$ | 7.94 | 7.72* 8.22† | 8.10 | 8.10 |
| Reduced Viscosity (ml/g) | 4.07 | 3.92* 3.81† | 3.4 | 3.7 |
| Molecular Weight | 34,700 | 35,300* 30,000† | 34,100 | 34,000 |
| Partial Specific Volume | 0.726 | 0.743* 0.726† | 0.732 | 0.742 |
| Isoelectric Point | 6.8 | 8.6 | 8.6 | 7.0 |
| Maximum Absorption ($m\mu$) | 277 | 2.77 | 277 | 277 |
| Extinction $\left(E^{1\%}_{1\,cm}\right)$ | 14.3 | 14.0* 14.4 | 12.1 | 12.1 |

*Schantz et al., 1965.
†Bergdoll et al., 1965b.

The sedimentation coefficients ($s_{20,w}$) were found to be essentially
the same for the different enterotoxins.  A valve-type, synthetic-
boundary cell was also used in measuring diffusion coefficients
($D_{20,w}$) with one exception.   The diffusion coefficient for enterotoxin B reported by Bergdoll et al. (1965b) was obtained by the
agar gel method of Schantz and Lauffer (1962).  The use of this
method apparently resulted in higher values than those obtained
with the synthetic boundary cells method.

   The intrinsic viscosity of the enterotoxins varies from 3.4 ml/g
for enterotoxin $C_1$ to 4.07 ml/g for enterotoxin A.  The measurements made in the Food Research Institute laboratories for all of
the enterotoxins were performed with a 0.5 ml capillary viscosimeter as described by Schachman (1957), while Wagman et al.
(1965) measured the intrinsic viscosity of enterotoxin B with a
calibrated Cannon-Fenske capillary viscosimeter.  Investigators
in both laboratories dissolved the enterotoxins in 0.05 M sodium
phosphate at pH 6.8.  The values obtained in the two laboratories
for enterotoxin B are in good agreement.

The partial specific volumes for enterotoxins B, $C_1$, and $C_2$ were determined by pycnometry and also calculated from the amino acid composition. From the results that have been reported, it would appear that calculation from the amino acid composition according to the method of Schachman (1957) may be more reliable than the values obtained by pycnometry. For enterotoxin B, the value of 0.726 reported by Bergdoll et al. (1965b) and the value of 0.731 reported by Spero et al. (1965), both calculated from the respective amino acid compositions determined by the two groups, are lower than the value 0.743 obtained by pycnometry by Wagman et al. (1965). E. J. Schantz (personal communication), on rechecking the partial specific volume for enterotoxin B, reports that the experimental value he obtained by pycnometry was 0.730, which is in agreement with the values calculated from the amino acid composition. The value 0.732 obtained for enterotoxin $C_1$ by pycnometry is in good agreement with the value 0.728 calculated from the amino acid composition, but the value 0.742 for $C_2$ obtained by pycnometry does not agree with the value 0.725 calculated from the amino acid composition.

The molecular weight of 34,500 calculated for enterotoxin A from the $s_{20,w}^O$ value of 3.04 S, the $D_{20,w}^O$ value of $7.94 \times 10^{-7}$ cm$^2$ sec$^{-1}$, and the apparent partial specific volume ($\overline{V}$) 0.726 ml/g in the Svedberg equation M = $RTs/D(1-\overline{V}p)$ is in good agreement with the value of 34,200 obtained from the approach to equilibrium studies using Archibald's method as modified by Ehrenberg (1957), and the value of 34,700 ± 1000 calculated from the amino acid composition (Chu et al., 1966). The molecular weight 30,800 calculated for enterotoxin B from the $s_{20,w}^O$ value of 2.78 S, the $D_{20,w}^O$ value of $8.22 \times 10^{-7}$ cm$^2$ sec$^{-1}$, and the apparent partial specific volume ($\overline{V}$) 0.726 mg/g in the Svedberg equation is in good agreement with the value of 30,500 obtained from the $s_{20,w}^O$ value of 2.78 S and $\eta$ value of 3.81 using the formula M = $4690 (s_{20,w}^O)^{3/2}(\eta)^{1/2}/(1 - \overline{V}p)^{3/2}$ and the value of 30,000 ± 1000 calculated from the half-cystine content of the enterotoxin and the minimum molecular weight values for the other amino acids (Bergdoll et al., 1965b). These results are lower than the molecular weights of 35,300 calculated by Wagman et al. (1965) from the $s_{20,w}^O$, $D_{20,w}^O$ and $\overline{V}$ values 2.89 S, $7.72 \times 10^{-7}$ cm$^2$ sec$^{-1}$, and 0.743 in the Svedberg equation, and of 35,100 obtained by the Archibald method, and the molecular weight of 35,380 calculated by Spero et al. (1965) from the amino acid composition. This discrepancy is being rechecked by E. J. Schantz (personal communication), and preliminary information indicates the molecular weight to be near 32,000.

The molecular weights for enterotoxin $C_1$ and $C_2$ have been calculated to be 34,100 and 34,000 from the $s_{20,w}^O$, $D_{20,w}^O$ and $\overline{V}$ values given in Table 4 using the Svedberg equation. These are in good agreement with the values of 34,050 for $C_1$ and 33,900 for $C_2$ ob-

tained from the amino acid composition (Huang et al., 1967).
Calculation of the molecular weights of these two enterotoxins
by the Archibald method has not been completed.

Theoretical speculation on the effective sizes and shapes of
proteins in solution is provided by a β-function given by the equation of Scheraga and Mandelkern (1953). According to the table
presented by them, a value of $\beta > 2.15 \times 10^6$ rules out the possibility of an oblate ellipsoid. Because the β-values obtained for
the enterotoxins (A = 2.24, B = 2.14, $C_1$ = 2.17, $C_2$ = 2.23) are
greater than $2.15 \times 10^6$, except for enterotoxin B, it is reasonable to assume that the shape of the enterotoxin molecule is a
prolate ellipsoid. Data on axial and frictional ratios for the purified enterotoxins indicate molecular compactness.

All of the enterotoxins have a maximum absorption at 277 mμ
with extinctions $\left(E_{cm}^{1\%}\right)$ of around 14 for enterotoxins A and B as
compared to extinctions of around 12 for $C_1$ and $C_2$. Bergdoll
et al. (1965b) reported an extinction of 15 for enterotoxin B based
on a nitrogen value obtained by an analytical laboratory; however,
redetermination of the nitrogen content with an F & M Scientific
Model 185 carbon hydrogen nitrogen analyzer yielded a higher
nitrogen value for the enterotoxin B preparation. Calculation of
the extinction from the nitrogen content obtained by this method
gave a value of 14.4, which is near the 14.0 reported by Schantz
et al. (1965).

The isoelectric point for enterotoxin B was determined by
Hibnick and Bergdoll (1959) with a modified Klett type of the U-
tube apparatus developed by Tiselius to be 8.6. This was confirmed by Schantz et al. (1965) with a Spinco Model H electrophoresis apparatus. The isoelectric points of the other enterotoxins were calculated from paper electrophoresis experiments
(Avena and Bergdoll, 1967; Borja and Bergdoll, 1967; Chu et al.,
1966).

The lower isoelectric points of enterotoxins A and $C_2$ do affect
the conditions for adsorption of these enterotoxins by CM-cellulose
because they are less readily adsorbed than B and $C_1$, which have
much higher isoelectric points. The difference in adsorption of
$C_1$ and $C_2$ on CM-cellulose and the dissimilarity in their electrophoretic mobilities is the basis for differentiation of these two
enterotoxins.

According to the calculations of Spero et al. (1965), there is an
apparent excess of eight basic groups in the enterotoxin B molecule, requiring the titration of all the histidine residues and two
of the lysine residues to achieve electrical neutrality. From
these data, they calculated an isoionic point of 8.70, which is in
good agreement with experimental values of 8.6 for the isoelectric
point and 8.55 for the isoionic point (Schantz et al., 1965). Chu
et al. (1966) calculated an excess of four basic groups for entero-

toxin A.  They assumed that the excess basic groups were due to four imidazole groups of the histidine residues existing in the un-dissociated form at the isoionic or isoelectric points.  They based their assumption on the pK value 6.3 to 6.9 (1962) for the imidazole group of the histidine residue.  The amino acid analyses for en-terotoxins $C_1$ and $C_2$ indicate an excess of eight basic groups for $C_1$ and an excess of four basic groups for $C_2$ (Huang et al., 1967) which corresponds to the calculated isoelectric points for these two proteins.

## Homogeneiety of the Enterotoxins

In velocity ultracentrifugation, solutions of each of the purified enterotoxins exhibited only a single symmetrical sedimenting boundary.  Free electrophoresis studies in the case of enterotoxin B and paper electrophoresis studies in the case of enterotoxins A, $C_1$, and $C_2$ showed the enterotoxins to be single components.  All of the enterotoxin preparations were shown to be of 95 per cent purity or better by the double gel-diffusion method.  This method has been modified for the detection of very small amounts of im-purities (0.1 per cent) in purified protein preparations by varying the concentration of both the enterotoxin and the antisera (Bergdoll et al., 1959a; Bergdoll et al., 1965a).  Usually the concentration of the enterotoxins employed ranges from 2 mg to 1 μg/ml, and the concentration of the antisera (from partially purified entero-toxin) ranges from a one-plus-one dilution to a dilution that re-sults in a visible precipitin band with 1 μg of the enterotoxin.  The minimal enterotoxin concentration at which a precipitin band ap-pears as a result of the presence of an impurity is compared to the minimal enterotoxin concentration that is required to produce a precipitin band to the enterotoxin.  The relationship of the two concentrations gives a rough estimate of the impurity concentra-tion.

Baird-Parker and Joseph (1964) reported that purified entero-toxin B prepared by the methods of Bergdoll et al. (1959a) and Schantz et al. (1965) separated into two main components during electrophoresis in starch gel at pH 8.5 and pH. 8.68.  Both com-ponents reacted with the specific antibody to enterotoxin B; how-ever, only one component caused vomiting when injected intra-peritoneally into piglets.  Schantz et al. (1965) reported that electrophoresis in starch gel using 0.02 M borate buffer at pH 8.6 showed two major components that moved toward the cathode.  In borate or Veronal buffer at pH 8.6 and in 0.02 M phosphate buf-fer at pH 7.0 containing NaCl to bring the ionic strength to 0.1 only a single band was obtained.  Both components obtained with the 0.02 M borate buffer at pH 8.6 showed toxicity in monkeys and gel-diffusion values equal to that of the original toxin.  In a later publication, Joseph and Baird-Parker (1965) suggested that changes

in the secondary or tertiary protein configuration may have caused
the formation of the two bands.   Other data indicate that conforma-
tional changes take place as the toxin ages, and two components
are evident in chromatography on CM-cellulose, both with the same
biological activity (Sumyk et al., 1966).   Separation into two bands
in starch-gel electrophoresis has also been reported for enterotoxins A (Chu et al., 1966) and $C_1$ (Borja and Bergdoll, 1967).

## Amino Acid Composition

The amino acid compositions of enterotoxins A, B, $C_1$, and $C_2$
were determined in the Food Research Institute laboratories with
a Spinco Model 120 B amino acid analyzer (Bergdoll et al., 1965b;
Huang et al., 1967; Huang et al., 1966a) (Table 5).   Hydrolysates
were prepared by heating in 6 N HCl at 110°C for 12, 24, 36, and
60 hours in evacuated, sealed tubes.   The values for threonine,
serine, and amide nitrogen were determined by extrapolation to
zero time.   Cystine was determined with the analyzer after con-
verting cystine to cysteic acid by performic acid oxidation followed
by hydrolysis of the oxidized enterotoxin (Hirs, 1956).   Tryptophan
was determined by the method of Beaven and Holiday (1952).

The amino acid composition and the number of amino acid residues
for each of the enterotoxins are given in Tables 5 and 6.   Enterotoxin A contains less lysine, aspartic acid, and methionine and more
arginine, glutamic acid, leucine, and tryptophan than the other enterotoxins.   It is not known whether these differences have any significance as far as the activity and stability of the molecule is concerned.   Spero et al. (1965) have also determined the amino acid
composition of enterotoxin B (Table 5).   The results they reported
are essentially the same as those obtained in the Food Research
Institute laboratories.

## Terminal Amino Acids of the Enterotoxins

Spero et al. (1965) reported that the N- and C-terminal amino
acids for enterotoxin B are glutamic acid and lysine, respectively.
The N-terminal amino acid was determined by the fluorodinitroben-
zene technique of Sanger (1945).   Chromatographic examination of
the ether extracts of the hydrolysate of the DNP-toxin were done by
the two-dimensional system of Levy (1955) and the unidimensional
system of Blackburn and Lowther (1951).   The C-terminal amino
acid was determined by hydrazinolysis by the method of Niu and
Fraenkel-Conrat (1955) as modified by Spero et al. (1965).   These
workers used the amino acid analyzer after the reaction with benzaldehyde.   The terminal amino acids for all of the enterotoxins as determined by Food Research Institute investigators (Bergdoll et al.,
1965b; Huang et al., 1967; Huang et al., 1966a) with essentially
the same methods used by Spero et al. (1965) are given in Table 7.

Table 5.   Amino Acid Composition of the Enterotoxins

| Amino Acid | Amino Acid residues 1/100 g protein (g) | | | |
| --- | --- | --- | --- | --- |
| | Enterotoxin A | Enterotoxin B | Enterotoxin $C_1$ | Enterotoxin $C_2$ |
| Lysine | 11.32 | 15.25* | 14.85† | 14.43 | 13.99 |
| Histidine | 2.86 | 2.45 | 2.34 | 2.91 | 2.87 |
| Arginine | 3.99 | 2.67 | 2.69 | 1.71 | 1.75 |
| Aspartic Acid | 15.75 | 17.93 | 18.13 | 17.85 | 18.38 |
| Threonine | 6.28 | 4.69 | 4.50 | 5.31 | 5.80 |
| Serine | 3.90 | 4.23 | 4.05 | 4.58 | 4.81 |
| Glutamic Acid | 11.65 | 9.55 | 9.45 | 8.95 | 8.93 |
| Proline | 1.82 | 2.10 | 2.11 | 2.16 | 2.23 |
| Glycine | 3.56 | 1.90 | 1.78 | 2.99 | 2.90 |
| Alanine | 2.19 | 1.37 | 1.32 | 1.85 | 1.61 |
| Half-Cystine | 0.62 | 0.58 | 0.68 | 0.79 | 0.74 |
| Valine | 4.95 | 5.49 | 5.66 | 6.50 | 5.87 |
| Methionine | 1.11 | 3.70 | 3.52 | 3.20 | 3.60 |
| Isoleucine | 4.34 | 3.45 | 3.53 | 4.09 | 4.02 |
| Leucine | 8.68 | 6.37 | 6.86 | 6.54 | 6.13 |
| Tyrosine | 10.09 | 11.20 | 11.50 | 9.80 | 10.27 |
| Phenylalanine | 5.12 | 6.12 | 6.23 | 5.35 | 5.25 |
| Tryptophan | 1.71 | 1.05 | 0.95 | 0.99 | 0.84 |
| Amide $NH_3$ | 1.66 | 1.58 | 1.66 | 1.71 | 1.62 |
| Total | 99.94 | 100.10 | 100.15 | 100.00 | 99.99 |

*Column 2, Spero et al., 1965.
†Column 3, Bergdoll et al., 1965b.

Table 6.   Amino Acid Composition of the Enterotoxins

| Amino Acid | No. Amino Acid Residues | | | |
|---|---|---|---|---|
| | Enterotoxin A (35,700) | Enterotoxin B (35,380)* (30,000)† | Enterotoxin $C_1$ (34,100) | Enterotoxin $C_2$ (34,000) |
| Lysine | 31 | 42 | 35 | 38 | 37 |
| Histidine | 7 | 6 | 5 | 7 | 7 |
| Arginine | 9 | 6 | 5 | 4 | 4 |
| Aspartic Acid | 48 | 55 | 47 | 53 | 54 |
| Threonine | 22 | 16 | 13 | 18 | 20 |
| Serine | 16 | 17 | 14 | 18 | 19 |
| Glutamic Acid | 32 | 26 | 22 | 24 | 24 |
| Proline | 7 | 8 | 7 | 8 | 8 |
| Glycine | 22 | 12 | 9 | 18 | 17 |
| Alanine | 11 | 7 | 5 | 9 | 8 |
| Half-Cystine | 2 | 2 | 2 | 2 | 2 |
| Valine | 18 | 20 | 17 | 22 | 20 |
| Methionine | 3 | 10 | 8 | 8 | 9 |
| Isoleucine | 13 | 11 | 9 | 12 | 12 |
| Leucine | 27 | 20 | 18 | 20 | 18 |
| Tyrosine | 22 | 24 | 21 | 21 | 21 |
| Phenylalanine | 12 | 15 | 13 | 12 | 12 |
| Tryptophan | 3 | 2 | 2 | 2 | 2 |
| Amide $NH_2$ | 37 | 35 | 29 | 36 | 34 |
| Total | 305 | 299 | 252 | 296 | 294 |

*Spero et al., 1965.
†Bergdoll et al., 1965b.

Table 7.  N- and C-terminal Amino Acids of the Enterotoxins

| Enterotoxin | N-terminal Amino Acid | C-terminal Amino Acid |
|:---:|:---:|:---:|
| A | Alanine | Serine |
| B | Glutamic acid | Lysine |
| C (137) | Glutamic acid | Glycine |
| C (361) | Glutamic acid | Glycine |

As will be noted, enterotoxins B, $C_1$, and $C_2$ have the same N-terminal amino acid, glutamic acid, while $C_1$ and $C_2$ have the same C-terminal amino acid, glycine.  The terminal amino acids of enterotoxin A are different from those of the other enterotoxins. The conclusion that alanine is the N-terminal amino acid is tentative because the recovery of this amino acid was below what would be expected for alanine; however, it was the only amino acid recovered in more than trace amounts.

Bergdoll et al. (1965b) determined the N-terminal amino acid sequence of enterotoxin B to be glutamic acid-serine-aspartic acid-lysine- by Edman's PTC procedure as modified by Fraenkel-Conrat et al. (1955) and by leucine aminopeptidase treatment followed by paper chromatography.  These workers determined the C-terminal amino acid sequence to be lysine-lysine-tyrosine-leucine- by modification of the hydrozinolytic procedure of Akabori et al. (1956) and by treatment with carboxypeptidases A and B.

Treatment of enterotoxin B alternately three times with carboxypeptidases A and B resulted in the removal of 20 to 22 amino acid residues from the C-terminal end of the enterotoxin molecule before proline appears in the chain (Table 8).  The enterotoxin residue that was recovered by CM-cellulose chromatrography reacted with the specific antibody to enterotoxin B without any observable change and was toxic to monkeys.

Studies are under way in the Food Research Institute laboratories to determine the amino acid sequence of enterotoxin B (Huang et al., 1966b).  In these studies, the enterotoxin is oxidized with performic acid according to the method of Hirs (1956), except that 1.5 times the amount of performic acid used in the original method is added in order to oxidize the methionine completely before treatment with the various proteolytic enzymes.  The amino acid composition of 21 peptides isolated after tryptic digestion of the oxidized enterotoxin B have been determined; however, the total number of amino acid residues found in these peptides accounts for only 50% of the amino acid residues calculated for this enterotoxin.

Table 8. Liberation of Amino Acids from Enterotoxin B
by Treatment with Carboxypeptidases B, A, and
A + B, Respectively

| Amino Acid | Moles of Amino Acid Liberated per Mole of Enterotoxin B Enzyme Treatment, 5 hours at 30°C | | | | |
|---|---|---|---|---|---|
| | Cpase B 1:500 | Cpase A 1:25 | Cpase A+B 1:25 | Cpase A+B 1:25 | Total Moles |
| Lysine | 1.05 | 0.13 | 1.03 | 0.68 | 2.99 |
| Tyrosine | 0.17 | 0.14 | 0.67 | 0.94 | 1.92 |
| Leucine | 0.16 | 0.14 | 0.58 | 0.71 | 1.59 |
| Serine | 0.09 | 0.20 | 0.34 | 0.58 | 1.21 |
| Phenylalanine | 0.10 | 0.08 | 0.27 | 0.55 | 1.00 |
| Valine | 0.08 | 0.12 | 0.20 | 0.45 | 0.95 |
| Threonine | 0.10 | 0.10 | 0.27 | 0.32 | 0.79 |
| Isoleucine | 0.08 | 0.10 | 0.22 | 0.29 | 0.69 |
| Alanine | 0.09 | 0.08 | 0.16 | 0.24 | 0.57 |
| Glutamic Acid | 0.09 | 0.08 | 0.10 | 0.13 | 0.40 |
| Aspartic Acid | 0.10 | 0.08 | 0.10 | 0.21 | 0.49 |
| Glycine | trace | 0.08 | 0.10 | 0.21 | 0.39 |
| Histidine | trace | trace | 0.15 | 0.24 | 0.39 |
| Methionine | trace | trace | 0.15 | 0.21 | 0.36 |
| Arginine | trace | trace | 0.22 | trace | 0.22 |

Dalidowicz et al. (1966) found the single disulfide bridge in enterotoxin B to be nonessential for biological activity and conformation of the protein. Reduction of the disulfide bridge and alkylation of the SH groups with both iodoacetamide and iodoacetate produced derivatives that had the same emetic activity as the native enterotoxin when administered intravenously to monkeys. The physical properties of the alkylated enterotoxins, as measured by viscosity and sedimentation, remained essentially the same as that of the native enterotoxin. Treatment with 6 M guanidine hydrochloride had no effect on the biological activity. Avena and Bergdoll (1967) also found that guanidine hydrochloride had no effect on the biological activity of enterotoxin $C_2$.

From present information about the enterotoxins, it is evident that they are simple proteins composed solely of amino acids. The fact that only one N- and one C-terminal amino acid has been detected for each enterotoxin indicates they are single polypeptide chains. Studies on the conformation of the enterotoxins indicate that they are compact molecules. There are no free SH groups and only one disulfide bridge is present, the latter being nonessential for biological activity and conformation of the protein.

## References

Akabori, S., et al., 1956, Bull. Chem. Soc. (Japan), 29, 507.

Avena, R. M., and M. S. Bergdoll, 1967. Biochemistry, 6 (No. 5).

Baird-Parker, A. C., and R. L. Joseph, 1964, Nature, 202, 510.

Beaven, G. H., and E. R. Holiday, 1952, Advan. Protein Chem., 7, 319.

Bergdoll, M. S., 1962, Proc. 14th Research Conference, American Meat Institute Foundation, Circular No. 70, p. 47.

Bergdoll, M.S., 1966. Unpublished data.

Bergdoll, M. S., C. R. Borja, and R. M. Avena, 1965, J. Bacteriol., 90, 1481.

Bergdoll, M. S., F. S. Chu, I-Y. Huang, C. Rowe, and T. Shih, 1965b, Arch. Biochem. Biophys., 112, 104.

Bergdoll, M. S., J. L. Kadavy, M. J. Surgalla, and G. M. Dack, 1951, Arch. Biochem. Biophys., 33, 259.

Bergdoll, M. S., B. Lavin, M. J. Surgalla, and G. M. Dack, 1952, Science, 116, 633.

Bergdoll, M. S., H. Sugiyama, and G. M. Dack, 1959a, Arch. Biochem. Biophys., 85, 62.

Bergdoll, M. S., H. Sugiyama, and G. M. Dack, 1961, J. Biochem. Microbiol. Technol. Eng., 3, 41.

Bergdoll, M. S., M. J. Surgalla, and G. M. Dack, 1959b, J. Immunol., 83, 334.

Blackburn, S., and A. G. Lowther, 1951, Biochem. J., 48, 126.

Borja, C. R., and M. S. Bergdoll, 1967. Biochemistry, 6 (No. 5).

Casman, E. P., 1958, Public Health Reports, 73, 599.

Casman, E. P., 1960, J. Bacteriol., 79, 849.

Casman, E. P., and R. W. Bennett, 1963, J. Bacteriol., 86, 18.

Casman, E. P., and R. W. Bennett, 1964, Appl. Microbiol., 12, 363.

Casman, E. P., and R. W. Bennett, 1965, Appl. Microbiol., 13, 181.

Casman, E. P., R. W. Bennett, and E. R. Kephart, 1966, Bacteriol. Proc., p. 13.

Casman, E. P., M. S. Bergdoll, and J. Robinson, 1963, J. Bacteriol., 85, 715.

Chu, F. S., K. Thadhani, E. J. Schantz, and M. S. Bergdoll, 1966, Biochemistry, 5, 3281.

Dack, G. M., W. E. Cary, O. Woolpert, and H. J. Wiggers, 1930, Prevent. Med., 4, 167.

Dalidowicz, J. E., S. J. Silverman, E. J. Schantz, D. Stefanye, and L. Spero, 1966, Biochemistry, 5, 237.

Darrach, M. D., 1941, Ph.D. Thesis, University of Toronto, Canada.

Davison, E., 1940, Ph.D. Thesis, University of Chicago, Illinois.

Davison, E., G. M. Dack, and W. E. Cary, 1938, J. Infect. Dis., 62, 219.

Denny, C. B., and C. W. Bohrer, 1963, J. Bacteriol., 86, 347.

Dolman, C. E., 1943, Canad. Pub. Health J., 34, 97, 205.

Dolman, C. E., R. J. Wilson, and W. H. Cockcroft, 1936, Canad. Pub. Health J., 27, 489.

Eddy, C. A., 1951, Proc. Soc. Exptl. Biol. Med., 78, 131.

Ehrenberg, A., 1957, Acta Chem. Scand., 11, 1257.

Favorite, G. O., and W. McD. Hammon, 1941, J. Bacteriol., 41, 305.

Finney, D. J., 1952, Probit. Analysis, London, Cambridge.

Fraenkel-Conrat, H., J. I. Harris, and A. L. Levy, 1955, Methods Biochem. Anal., 2, 359.

Frea, J. I., E. McCoy, and F. M. Strong, 1963, J. Bacteriol., 86, 1308.

Friedman, M. E., and J. D. White, 1965, J. Bacteriol., 89, 1155.

Genigeorgis, C., and W. W. Sadler, 1966, J. Food Sci., 31, 605.

Hall, H. E., R. Angelotti, and K. H. Lewis, 1963, Public Health Reports, 78, 1089.

Hall, H. E., R. Angelotti, and K. H. Lewis, 1965, Health Lab. Sci., 2, 179.

Hammon, W. McD., 1941, Amer. J. Pub. Health, 31, 1191.

Hibnick, H. E., and M. S. Bergdoll, 1959, Arch. Biochem. Biophys., 85, 70

Hirs, C. H. W., 1956, J. Biol. Chem., 219, 611.

Hopkins, E. W., and E. F. Poland, 1942, J. Bacteriol., 43, 267.

Hopper, S. H., 1963, J. Food Science, 28, 572.

Huang, I-Y., F. S. Chu, T. Shih, and M. S. Bergdoll, 1966a. Unpublished data.

Huang, I-Y., T. Shih, and M. S. Bergdoll, 1966b. Unpublished data.

Huang, I-Y., T. Shih, C. R. Borja, R. M. Avena, and M. S. Bergdoll, 1967. Biochemistry, 6 (No. 5).

Jordan, E. O., and J. McBroom, 1931, Proc. Soc. Exptl. Biol. Med., 29, 161.

Joseph, R. L., and A. C. Baird-Parker, 1965, Nature, 207, 663.

Kato, E., M. Khan, L. Kujovich, and M. S. Bergdoll, 1966, Appl. Microbiol., 14, 966.

Levy, A. L., 1955, Methods Biochem. Anal., 2, 360.

Minett, F. C., 1938, J. Hyg., 38, 623.

Nikodemusz, I., L. Kanizsai, and E. Sellei, 1962, Acta Medica, 19, 209.

Niu, C-I., and H. Fraenkel-Conrat, 1955, J. Amer. Chem. Soc., 77, 5882.

Read, R. B. Jr., W. L. Pritchard, J. Bradshaw, and L. A. Black, 1965a, J. Dairy Sci., 48, 411.

Read, R. B. Jr., W. L. Pritchard, J. Bradshaw, and L. A. Black, 1965b, J. Dairy Sci., 48, 420.

Robinson, J., and F. S. Thatcher, 1965, Bacteriol. Proc., p. 72.

Robinton, E. D., 1950, Yale J. Biol. Med., 23, 94.

Sanger, F., 1945, Biochem. J., 39, 507.

Schachman, H. K., 1957, Methods of Enzymology, (S. P. Colowick and N. O. Kaplan, Editors), Academic Press, New York, Vol. 4, p. 32.

Schachman, H. K., 1959, Ultracentrifugation in Biochemistry, Academic Press, New York, p. 186.

Schantz, E. J., and M. A. Lauffer, 1962, Biochemistry, 1, 658.

Schantz, E. J., W. G. Roessler, J. Wagman, L. Spero, D. A. Dunnery, and M. S. Bergdoll, 1965, Biochemistry, 4, 1011.

Scheraga, H. A., and L. Mandelkern, 1953, J. Amer. Chem. Soc., 75, 179.

Spero, L., D. Stefanye, P. I. Brecher, H. M. Jacoby, J. E. Dalidowicz, and E. J. Schantz, 1965, Biochemistry, 4, 1024.

Sugiyama, H., 1966, J. Infect. Dis., 116, 162.

Sugiyama, H., M. S. Bergdoll, and R. G. Wilkerson, 1960, Proc. Soc. Exptl. Biol. Med., 103, 168.

Sumyk, G. B., W. G. Roessler, S. Silverman, and E. J. Schantz, 1966. Unpublished data.

Surgalla, M. J., M. S. Bergdoll, and G. M. Dack, 1952, J. Immunol., 69, 357.

Surgalla, M. J., M. S. Bergdoll, and G. M. Dack, 1953, J. Lab. Clin. Med., 41, 782.

Surgalla, M. J., and G. M. Dack, 1955, J. Amer. Med. Assoc., 158, 649.

Surgalla, M. J., J. L. Kadavy, M. S. Bergdoll, and G. M. Dack, 1951, J. Infect. Dis., 89, 180.

Tanford, C., 1962, Advances in Protein Chemistry, Academic Press, Inc., New York, Vol. 17, p. 112.

Wagman, J., R. C. Edwards, and E. J. Schantz, 1965, Biochemistry, 4, 1017.

Weirether, F. J., E. E. Lewis, A. J. Rosenwald, and R. E. Lincoln, 1966, Appl. Microbiol., 14, 284.

# CHEMISTRY AND BIOLOGICAL ACTIVITY OF THE TOXIN OF CLOSTRIDIUM BOTULINUM

D. A. Boroff, B. R. Das Gupta, U. Fleck
Albert Einstein Medical Center, Laboratory of Immunology
Philadelphia, Pennsylvania

Much has been written about the toxin of Clostridium botulinum. There is still, however, only scant knowledge of the chemistry, mode of action, or the site of its action of this remarkable substance. The toxin is elaborated by C. botulinum of which six serologic types are known. The organism is an anaerobe, widely spread in the soil, that becomes toxigenic only under certain special conditions. The disease is a result of the ingestion of the preformed toxin. Once a lethal dose has been ingested, very little can be done for the affected animal or man. The antitoxin, unless administered very early after intoxication, is not very effective, and there are no other substances or drugs known that will counteract the lethal action of the toxin. Even if the animal survives, convalescense is prolonged and difficult. The only sure protection against this disease is prophylactic immunization. Vaccines available at present, however, are still in development stages.

Neurological symptoms invariably observed in botulinum intoxication directed attention to various functional disturbances that could be demonstrated in the peripheral nervous system (Schubel, 1921). The particular sites of action were, however, described by Dickson and Shevky (1923) who pointed out the similarity between the sites of action of the botulinum toxin and those of acetylcholine. They further showed that motor paralysis was not due to blocking impulses along the nerve trunk but was dependent upon the intoxication of some end-organ (myoneural junction). This was later confirmed by Guyton and MacDonald (1947) and Ambache (1949). However, the manner in which botulinum toxin interferes with acetylcholine release at the neuromuscular junction still remains obscure; Brooks (1954) observed that the acetylcholine release mechanism is not in itself damaged. Nonetheless, all evidence so far accumulated show that botulinum toxin acts on those portions of the peripheral nervous system that are cholinergic, whether they are pre- or postganglionic components of the nervous system. These may not be the only effects of botulinum toxin because in clinical and laboratory botulism there are indications that the central nervous system is also involved (Matveev, 1959). Furthermore, Winbury (1959) reported that botulinum toxin, besides affecting the cells of the striated muscles, also had an effect upon the smooth muscles of the blood vessels.

The exceptional lethality of this toxin places it in a unique position among bacterial and other poisons. About $10^{-5}$ µg is sufficient to kill a 20-gram mouse. Due to its high toxicity and its ability to induce the formation of antitoxin, botulinum toxin was thought to be an exotoxin, that is, a substance secreted by the clostridia as a product of their metabolism. This hypothesis was disputed by Raynaud and Second (1949) and later by Boroff and Raynaud (1952), who succeeded in obtaining by the extraction of washed organisms a toxin as powerful as that found in the culture filtrates. It was further established that a relationship existed between the rate of autolysis of the clostridia and the accumulation of toxin in the culture, which suggested the probability that the toxin is a part of the bacterial soma (Boroff, 1955; Gendon, 1957; Bouisset et al., 1957; Bonventre and Kempe, 1960). The homogeneity of the crystalline toxin also became questionable when Lamanna and Lowenthal (1951) reported that the toxin contained a separable component responsible for hemagglutinating properties previously thought to be property of the pure toxin.

Working with the toxin of C. botulinum Type C, we observed that the toxin fluoresces in the near-ultraviolet region (350 mµ) when activated by the ultraviolet wavelength (285 mµ). Furthermore, procedures and reagents that destroyed fluorescence also destroyed toxicity, although destruction of toxicity was not invariably followed by the disappearance of fluorescence. This observation led us to the investigation of the fluorescence of botulinum toxin with the hope that, because fluorescence of a substance depends upon particular groups or structures of the molecule, careful study of this property as it is influenced by a variety of experimental procedures may lead to an understanding of the chemistry of the toxin, and thus, perhaps, to its mode of action. That the toxin fluoresces is not of itself remarkable. All proteins fluoresce owing to their constituent aromatic amino acids. Because the fluorescence is strongest in tryptophan, and because the toxin fluoresced at a wavelength characteristic of tryptophan, our attention was drawn to this amino acid.

Certain observations made by us and by other investigators also suggested that tryptophan might be a critical element in the active sites of this protein. One finding was that serotonin (5-hydroxytryptamine), a derivative of tryptophan, inhibits activity in vivo. L-Tryptophan also has this antitoxic property, but to a lesser degree. Another finding (Mager et al., 1954) was that to be toxigenic C. botulinum requires in the culture medium 10 times the amount

of tryptophan needed for growth alone.  Finally, toxicity and fluorescence were lost when the toxin was treated with formalin to
produce a toxoid.  Formation of the toxoid, according to Fraenkel-
Conrat, Brandon, and Olcott (1947) is caused by the condensation
of the tryptophan residues in two molecules of toxin.  Through
this process, the toxin, while losing its toxicity, is still able to
induce formation of antibodies against fully active toxin.

Few methods permit selective modification of an amino acid
residue in a protein without either affecting other structures in
the molecule or cleaving peptide bonds.  One method, described
by Weil, Gordon, and Buchart (1951) and Weil, James, and Buchart
(1951), is photooxidation by visible light catalyzed by methylene
blue, which modifies five amino acids: tryptophan, tyrosine, histidine, methionine, and cysteine.  Sluyterman (1962) recently reported that photooxidation of free amino acids in the presence of
proflavine is pH dependent, and that at acid pH (3.8 and lower) only
tryptophan and methionine are oxidized.  We showed that similar
results can be obtained by photooxidizing proteins in the presence
of methylene blue (Das Gupta and Boroff, 1965).

To study the effects of this process on botulinum toxin, 2.8 ml
of this solution, mixed with 0.5 ml of 0.02% methylene blue, was
placed into a water-cooled cell and exposed to three 150 W incan-
descent light bulbs.  Another aliquot was stored in the dark as a
control to be assayed at the end of the experiment.  At the end of
the first 30 minutes, the photooxidized sample was replaced by
another aliquot that was then exposed for 15 minutes longer than
the preceding sample.  Seven such samples were photooxidized,
each exposed for 15 minutes longer than its predecessor, with the
last sample exposed for 120 minutes.  Each sample was then assayed for toxicity by intravenous injection in mice and for fluorescence and residual concentration of the three photooxidation-
sensitive amino acids.  There was no attempt to assay for cysteine
because it was previously shown that this amino acid is not involved
in the toxicity of botulinum toxin (Schantz and Spero, 1957).

The toxin exposed to photooxidation showed no significant changes
in the concentration of either histidine or tyrosine.  There was a
gradual loss of toxicity that by the end of 120 minutes of photooxidation amounted to 90%.  During this period, about 25.8 moles out
of 77.2 moles of tryptophan present in a mole of toxin were also
destroyed.  Fluorescence in the wavelength of tryptophan decreased
from 72 to 35 fluorescent intensity (F.I.) units, or more than 50%.
Assay of the toxin photooxidized for the same 120 minutes showed,
however, a loss of 14.2 moles of methionine (Figure 1).

Two reagents, iodoacetate and $H_2O_2$, modify methionine prefer-
entially.  Addition of iodoacetate did not affect the toxin's activity.
However, these experiments were inconclusive because of the formation of chromophores that interfered with spectrophotometric

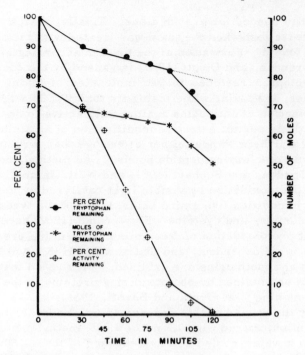

Fig. 1.   Effect of photooxidation on toxicity and destruction
         of tryptophan residues in the toxin of C. botulinum.
         (Boroff and Das Gupta, 1964.)

assay of methionine.   Therefore the effects of $H_2O_2$ on the toxin
were examined.   Neumann, Moore, and Stein (1962) have reported
that, at pH 2, $H_2O_2$ in the absence of halides does not effect tryptophan, and that peroxide is a reagent which selectively oxidized
methionine to methionine sulfoxide in ribonuclease.   Hydrogen
peroxide, 30%, was added to a solution of toxin that previously
had been adjusted to pH 2 by dialysis against 0.1 N $H_3PO_4$.   The
final concentration of the toxin solution was 1.0 mg of toxin (containing $7.0 \times 10^{-5}$ mmole of methionine) to 0.43 mmole of $H_2O_2$.
The solution was tested for toxicity without further treatment immediately after mixing (0 minutes) and after 30 minutes of incubation at 28°C.   A preliminary experiment revealed that this concentration of $H_2O_2$ was innocuous in mice when administered intravenously at the end of this period.   In order to titrate the residual
methionine, the solution was readjusted to pH 6 with 3 N NaOH
and the addition of 1.0% catalase in 4 µl portions at 2-minute intervals until its concentration reached 14 µl and the evolution of
gas ceased.   This procedure terminated the reaction.   The reaction and control solutions were subjected to alkaline hydrolysis
and assayed for methionine. There were no significant changes in
the preparations' toxicity during the entire period, but there was

a loss of 41.7 moles out of 62.8 moles of methionine per mole of
toxin after a 30-minute incubation with $H_2O_2$.  No significant
change in survival time was observed in either of the groups of
the injected mice (28 minutes for average of 6 mice in each group).
Ouchterlony double-diffusion tests performed with this preparation and, with untreated toxin as a control against rabbit antiserum prepared against the native toxin, showed that the photooxidized toxin reacted strongly with the serum; however, the tests
showed only one band instead of the two usually obtained with the
untreated preparations of the same protein concentration (Figure 2).

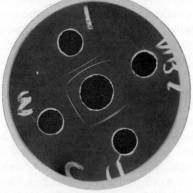

Fig. 2.   Ouchterlony gel double diffusion test with rabbit anti-
          serum prepared against photooxidized and 5-hydroxy-
          2-nitrobenzyl bromide treated toxins of C. botulinum
          Type A. Central well contains native crystalline toxin.
          Lateral wells, counterclockwise from upper right:
          well 1, antiserum to native toxin; well 2, photooxidized
          toxin; well 3, antiserum to 5-hydroxy-2-nitrobenzyl
          bromide treated toxin; well 4, normal rabbit serum
          control.

   Antiserum produced by injecting rabbits with toxoid formed from
photooxidized toxin failed to protect mice in a passive immunization test but reacted both with untreated and treated toxin in precipitation and complement fixation tests.  By Ouchterlony gel double-
diffusion technique, there was a loss of one precipitation line similar
to that observed with antiserum to untreated toxin reacted with photooxidized preparation.
   No categorical statement as to the role of tryptophan could be
made, however, until the question of the role of the remaining 34%
of methionine residues in the toxin could be clarified.  We therefore
searched for means to selectively modify tryptophan without affecting methionine.
   Recently Koshland, Karkhanis, and Latham (1964) described an
environmentally sensitive reagent with selectivity for the tryptophan

residues in proteins. This reagent, 2-hydroxy-5-nitrobenzyl
bromide (HNBB), according to these authors, substitutes in tryptophan and to a lesser degree in free -SH groups, leaving all other
amino acids unaffected. Because it had already been shown that
we need not be concerned with the question of participation of the
-SH groups in the activity of the toxin, it was resolved to examine
the effect of HNBB upon tryptophan residues and thus upon toxicity
and the antigenicity of the toxin of C. botulinum.

Twice-recrystallized toxin of C. botulinum Type A was used in
these experiments, and 2-hydroxy-5-nitrobenzyl bromide (HNBB)
was synthesized according to the method of Koshland et al. (1964).
The degree of substitution of HNBB in the tryptophan residues of
the toxin was estimated from values obtained for the residual amino
acid from assay by Spies and Chambers method (1949) by procedure
K for water-soluble proteins. Reaction 1 (after the addition of the
protein solution to p-dimethyl-aminobenzaldehyde in concentrated
$H_2SO_4$) was carried out for 24 hours at 28°C. Reaction 2 (after the
addition of $NaNO_2$ to the solution in reaction 1) was carried out for
30 minutes at the same temperature, and the reaction mixture's
extinction coefficient (at 590 mμ) was recorded.

Assay for other amino acids was performed by column chromatography. The material used was HNBB-reacted toxin precipitated
by trichloroacetic acid and hydrolyzed in constant-boiling-point
mixture of HCl for 16 hours at 121°C. Before hydrolysis, the TCA-
precipitated material was repeatedly washed in methanol to remove
excess HNBB until no yellow color absorbing at 410 mμ appeared
when the washings were made alkaline with NaOH. Protein deter-
minations were done by the method of Lowry, Rosebrough, Farr,
and Randall (1951). Toxicity of all preparations were estimated
from the survival time of mice injected intravenously with 0.1 ml
of the material.

To bring HNBB into solution, the desired amount was first dissolved in minimal amounts of methanol (0.05 to 0.1 ml) and then
mixed with the toxin solution. It was previously established that
these amounts of HNBB or methanol were not toxic for mice.

Antiserum to HNBB-treated toxin was obtained by intraperitoneal
injection of 1 ml of this toxin mixed with Freunds' adjuvant (Freund
and Bonanto, 1944) into female chinchilla rabbits, not less than 6
pounds each (Dierolf Farms, Inc., Boyertown, Pa.). Each received two such injections spaced 15 days apart. Fifteen days after
the last injection the rabbits were bled by cardiac puncture and the
serum separated. This serum was used in Ouchterlony gel double-
diffusion tests (Crowle, 1962) to examine the effects of HNBB upon
the antigenicity of the botulinum toxin.

To determine the effects of 2-hydroxy-5-nitrobenzyl bromide
(HNBB) upon crystalline botulinum toxin Type A, the toxin, 2.6 mg
per ml, was dialyzed for 16 hours against 0.01 N HCl. To 1.0 ml

of toxin solution at pH 2 was added 1.9 mg of HNBB in 0.05 ml
methanol and the mixture incubated at 27°C. At each one-half
hour an aliquot was withdrawn and assayed for toxicity. An equal
amount of toxin, also at pH 2, was mixed with 0.05 ml of methanol
and incubated under similar conditions. This preparation served
as a control. By periodic toxicity assays it was found that 99%
of the toxin was lost within the first half hour of incubation with
this amount of HNBB (Figure 3).

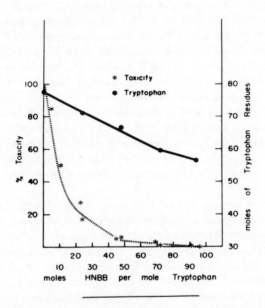

Fig. 3.   Effects of HNBB on toxicity and tryptophan residues
          of the toxin of C. botulinum Type A. Tryptophan
          assay by Spies and Chambers method. Toxicity as-
          say by intravenous injection in mice. (Boroff and
          Das Gupta, 1966.)

   In the next experiment, we determined the effect on the toxin
of increasing concentration of HNBB. To several portions of
2.42 mg of toxin, each contained in 1 ml of 0.01 N HCl, was added
HNBB in increasing concentration. The reaction mixtures, after
30 minutes' incubation, were assayed for toxicity and the content
of tryptophan determined. With the increasing amounts of HNBB,
there was a progressive loss of toxicity in the test preparations.
The content of tryptophan also decreased, showing linearity with
increasing amounts of HNBB up to 70 moles of the reagent per
mole of this amino acid. At this point about 99% of toxicity and
17.8 moles of tryptophan disappeared.
   In order to assay for other amino acids besides tryptophan, two
separate experiments were performed in which 5.2 ml of toxin so-

lution, containing 1.9 mg/ml, was reacted with 9.9 mg of HNBB. After 30 minutes' incubation, the mixture was treated with TCA. The assay revealed no significant changes in these amino acids as compared with similarly treated control solution of toxin but with no HNBB. This procedure did not yield reliable data for cysteine, cystine and methionine. The degree of reaction with HNBB with cysteine and methionine was therefore studied with the aid of performic acid oxidation by Moore's method (1963). In a separate experiment, toxin was reacted with HNBB as described earlier. The molar ratio of HNBB to tryptophan residues in the toxin was 72:1. The substituted toxin was separated from excess reagent by filtration on Sephadex G-25 column and dialysis as suggested by Koshland et al. (1964). The acid hydrolysates of performic acid oxidized reaction and control samples were analyzed by column chromatography to determine the total cysteic acid (cysteine and cystine) and methionine sulfone present. Results obtained showed a loss of 16.3 moles in cysteic acid content in the reaction sample. Because cystine does not react with HNBB (Koshland et al., 1964), this meant that HNBB substituted in 16.3 moles of -SH groups in the toxin. There was no significant change in the methionine content.

Serological reaction in Ouchterlony tests with antisera to untreated toxin and toxin inactivated by HNBB showed disappearance of one of the antibodies present in the former and demonstrable by reaction with the native toxin. The HNBB-treated toxin antiserum, when injected in 0.2 ml intravenously, or in 0.5 ml intraperitoneally into mice, failed to protect these animals against the injection of as little as 10 MLD of the toxin. Control mice, similarly treated with native antiserum, survived challenge of as much as $10^4$ MLD of the toxin. (See Figure 2.)

Results obtained by treating botulinum toxin with HNBB, with respect to toxicity loss, modification of tryptophan, and change in antigenicity, closely paralleled those obtained by photooxidizing the toxin. Because no other amino acid, including methionine, was affected, and because noninvolvement of cysteine in the toxicity of the protein has been discussed earlier, we may assume that the almost total loss of toxicity was due to the modification of tryptophan in the toxin.

The failure to induce protection with the injection of the treated toxin into rabbits and mice and the disappearance both of neutralizing and of one precipitating antibody from the serums of the rabbits, as shown by Ouchterlony's test, suggest two possible interpretations that may account for the observed phenomenon. One is that the crystalline toxin contains more than one component, one of which is toxin and the other an unrelated contaminant. Thus HNBB might have affected the tryptophan residue in the "contaminant" without affecting its antigenicity, while at the same time it may have acted on some structure other than tryptophan in the toxic

component resulting in activity loss. The other possibility is that
the toxin is homogeneous with two antigenic determinants located
on the same molecule, one capable of stimulating formation of
neutralizing and the other of precipitating antibody. The former
site might also be involved in the maintenance of toxicity by virtue
of the presence in this site of active tryptophan residues. Exposure of the toxin to photooxidation or treatment with HNBB results in the destruction of some active as well as inactive, but
available, tryptophan. This is followed by the loss of toxicity and
the ability to induce formation of neutralizing antibody, but without destroying the antigenic site responsible for precipitin formation.

Crystalline toxin of C. botulinum has been characterized as a
simple homogeneous protein of 900,000 molecular weight (Lamanna
et al., 1946; Putnam et al., 1946) and is thought to be an aggregate of smaller molecular weight units. On the basis of cysteine and cystine content, the minimum molecular weight of crystalline toxin was calculated as 45,000 (Buehler et al., 1947). In
an analytical ultracentrifuge at pH 9.2, this toxin sediments as two
components: one $s_{20,w}$ 7.3 and the second $s_{20,w}$ 13.7 (Wagman,
1963). From this study, Wagman (1963) suggested that these components were products of dissociation of the large aggregate. To
date, to our knowledge, there are no reports in the literature of
successful isolation and study of these components of the crystalline toxin.

Observations made in the course of our study of this substance
cast doubt as to the correctness of the suggested homogeneity, as
well as on the estimated molecular weight of this preparation.
This prompted an attempt to examine crystalline Type A toxin with
regard to these two parameters.

Crystalline toxin was chromatographed on DEAE-Sephadex,
equilibrated in 0.07 M tris-HCl buffer pH 7.2 and eluted in the
same buffer containing a gradient of NaCl. When the concentration of NaCl reached 0.1, a fraction ($\alpha$) emerged containing most
of the activity of the toxin but only 20% of the protein concentration of the original. On further elution, the remainder of the protein was recovered at 0.2 M NaCl concentration. This fraction
($\beta$) was only feebly toxic (Figure 4).

For rechromatography a portion of the eluate of each of the components was dialyzed against tris-HCl buffer to remove the excess
NaCl and recycled under identical conditions used in the original
procedure. Both components emerged at their previously observed
elution volume and Cl⁻ concentration. A small peak in the region
of $\beta$ emergence, which appeared on rechromatography of $\alpha$, was
no more detectable on subsequent recycling.

The isolated fractions were used to determine molecular weight
on Sephadex G-200 column by the method developed by Andrews
(1965), the validity of which has been confirmed by Siegel and

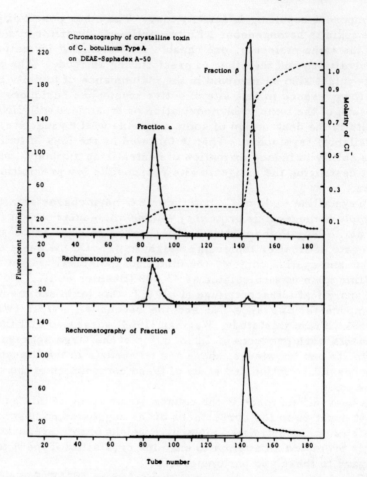

Fig. 4.  Chromatography of crystalline toxin of C. botulinum
          Type A on Sephadex A-50.  Top section: fractiona-
          tion of crystalline toxin.  Middle section: rechroma-
          tography of a portion of pooled α fraction obtained
          from first run.  Bottom section: rechromatography
          of a portion of pooled β fraction obtained from first
          run.  (Das Gupta et al., 1966.)

Monty (1965) and Soroff, Young, McBride, and Coffey (1966).  By
this method, components α and β appeared to have 150,000 molecular weight and 500,000 molecular weight, respectively.  By the
same procedure unfractionated crystalline toxin was of 740,000
molecular weight (Figure 5).  These components, when examined
in the analytical ultracentrifuge at pH 9.5, sedimented with $s_{20,w}$ = 7.2
for α and 13.1 for β.  As mentioned in the preceding paragraphs,
the molecular weight of crystalline toxin based on its $s_{20,w}$ (1946)
was established as 900,000.  Wagman (1963) found the $s_{20,w}$ for

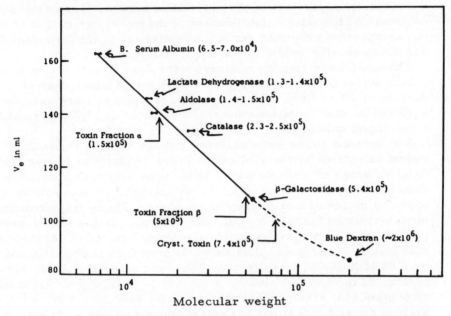

Fig. 5.   Molecular weights of proteins as determined by the
filtration on Sephadex G-200. Ve is the elution volume, plotted against log (molecular weight). Column
(2.5 cm × 50 cm) equilibrated and eluted with 0.05 M
tris-HCl buffer pH 7.5 containing 0.1 M HCl. Molecular weight of proteins indicated in parenthesis
in this experiment are according to Andrews (1965)
except for β-galactosidase, which is from Craven
et al. (1965). α and β components were from tubes
with the highest concentrations of these components
obtained after rechromatography. (Das Gupta et al.,
1966.)

the toxin at various pH and ionic concentration to be no more than
16.3. Thus the molecular weight for the unfractionated toxin of
740,000 is not inconsistent with the values ascribed to it by previous authors. On storage for as long as 30 days, either at 4°C
or at -28°C, α retained its molecular weight and toxicity as before storage.
By the Ouchterlony gel double-diffusion technique, each component reacted in a single precipitation line when tested against
rabbit anticrystalline toxin serum. Each of the lines corresponded
to one of the two precipitation lines obtained when this serum was
reacted with solution of the crystalline toxin. On electrophoresis
in 1% noble agar (Difco) on microscope slides at pH 8.6 tris-per-
chloric acid buffer 0.05 M for 7200 seconds at 8V/CM and 4°C, α
and β components exhibited different electrophoretic mobilities.

Successful separation of the crystalline toxin on chromatographic columns and tentative establishment of the molecular weight of the two components prompted further investigation of the homogeneity and the molecular weight in the ultracentrifuge.

Ultracentrifuge velocity analyses were done at 50,700 rpm in a Spinco Model E instrument equipped with temperature control. Aluminum-filled Epon cells with sapphire windows were used for equilibrium sedimentation runs that were done at 17,250 rpm with 3 mm liquid columns.

Interference plates were analyzed and equilibrium molecular weight calculated by the application of the Yphantis technique (1964). Relative areas of multiple peaks seen in the Schlieren runs were established by the projection of the photographs on heavy filter paper by means of a photographic enlarger. These projection patterns were then traced, cut out, and weighed. Buffers used were: acetate, sodium acetate molarity specified, titrated to desired pH with glacial acetic acid; phosphate, 63.6 ml 0.05 M $Na_2HPO_4$, 36.4 ml 0.05 M $NaH_2PO_4$ (resultant pH 7.0, ionic strength 0.227); carbonate, 92 ml 0.05 M $NaHCO_3$, 8 ml 0.05 M $NaHCO_3$, pH 9.3 ionic strength 0.116; tris-perchlorate, molarity specified, titrated to desired pH with 70% $HClO_4$. Protein concentrations were established by Lowry's method (Lowry et al., 1951).

Ultracentrifugal analysis was done on the crystalline toxin and the chromatographically separated fractions $\alpha$ and $\beta$. Examination of the data for the crystalline toxin shows distinct inhomogeneity with at least two peaks at every experimental condition employed. The experiments at the lower pH (3.8 to 7) were less reproducible than those at the higher pH (9 and above) because of large convective disturbances that could be seen moving ahead of the fast peaks. These disturbances, seen as transient spikes throughout the plateau region of the cell, indicated extensive interaction with solvent or buffer components (Cann and Goad, 1965). These disturbances were minimized or completely eliminated at alkaline pH's.

A common factor in all the experiments with the whole toxin was the presence of two major peaks with $s_{20,w}$ values near 7 and 13.5 S. This is in agreement with Wagman's findings (1963). The presence of a third component with S values near 16 indicate that these components (7 and 13.5) can undergo further aggregation. The aggregation to 16 S complex is probably reversible because increase in ionic strength from 0.02 to 0.05, with concomitant decreases in protein concentration from 2.7 to 1.9 mg/ml at the same pH (pH 9.5 tris-perchlorate), eliminated this peak entirely. That this is the case was also indicated by the observed reappearance of a 16 S peak at lower pH values, where even greater aggregation to material of 23 S was seen (Figure 6).

A single ultracentrifuge experiment was carried out at pH 9.5 in 5 M guanidine thiocyanate, which would be expected to act as a

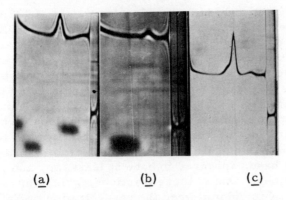

(a)　　　　　　(b)　　　　　　(c)

Fig. 6.　Ultracentrifuge photographs of crystalline toxin and
isolated fraction of C. botulinum Type A at 50,700
rpm, 32 minutes after reaching full speed, in 0.05
M tris-ClO$_4$, pH 9.5 at 25°C. (a) crystalline toxin;
(b) toxic fraction ($\alpha$); (c) nontoxic fraction ($\beta$).
(Boroff et al., 1966.)

dissociating agent (von Hippel and Wong, 1964). The 6 S peak,
however, completely disappeared and a peak with sedimentation
coefficient of 23.7 S appeared, in addition to 13 and 16 S peaks as
seen in other experiments. The isolated $\alpha$ and $\beta$ fractions, when
analyzed in the ultracentrifuge at pH 9, appeared to be homogeneous. At pH 3.8, however, the heavier $\beta$ component showed an
indication that it contained still heavier material. This is in agreement with results obtained with the whole toxin. There was, however, no evidence in all our experiments of any heterogeneity of
the $\alpha$ fraction, although the possibility that this fraction is a pol-
ymer and consists of smaller molecular weight units cannot yet be
ruled out. The $s_{20,w}$ values of fractions $\alpha$ and $\beta$ were identical
with $s_{20,w}$ values of the two peaks observed by Wagman (1963) who,
however, regarded them as dissociation products of the homogeneous crystalline toxin. Furthermore, the similarity of the $s_{20,w}$
values obtained on chromatographically separated fractions with
the values of the two major components seen in the crystalline toxin,
strongly indicates that these components were isolated without denaturation. This is corroborated by the observation that the $\alpha$ fraction, having only 20% of protein concentration of the crystalline
preparation, retained nearly 100% of the original toxicity.

Under no conditions did our experiments yield peaks with values
less than 6 S. This is in disagreement with the results reported
by Gerwing, Dolman, and Bains (1965).

The molecular weight of the toxic $\alpha$ fraction was established in
the ultracentrifuge, using the meniscus-depletion technique of
Yphantis (1964), in 0.05 M tris-perchlorate solvent at pH 9.5.
Equilibrium was attained in less than 24 hours. Data obtained

showed the fraction to have a molecular weight of 128,000 ± 10%.
This is in reasonable agreement with the value of 150,000 molecular weight obtained in our laboratory (Das Gupta et al., 1966)
by Andrews' method (1965) on Sephadex G-200, and value of
158,000 molecular weight assigned to this component by Wagman
(1963). The two components, $\alpha$ and $\beta$, were reacted by Ouchterlony technique along with the unfractionated toxin against the anticrystalline rabbit serum. The precipitation lines formed by the
antiserum and the two components show identity with lines formed
by crystalline toxin against the same antiserum. Component $\beta$,
on the other hand, appeared to have at least two, and perhaps
more, fractions. One of these fractions, which eluted from the
chromatographic column when the concentration of NaCl reached
0.2 M and diluted 1:320 in buffer, still strongly agglutinated red
blood cells. This component, therefore, appears to be hemagglu-
tinin, which has always been associated with the crystalline toxin
of C. botulinum Type A, and which has been described by Lamanna
et al. (1946).

Preliminary experiments with component $\alpha$ showed that upon
photooxidation by visible light in the presence of methylene blue,
there was a loss of fluorescence (therefore a loss in tryptophan)
and a loss of toxicity that were both related to the duration to exposure to light. The rate of loss of these two functions was similar to that observed in photooxidized or HNBB-treated preparations. Similarly, in the Ouchterlony test, photooxidized or HNBB-
treated component $\alpha$ failed to react with antiserum to crystalline
toxin.

These experiments, therefore, continue to support our hypothesis
that some tryptophan residues in the molecule of the toxin are of
critical importance to the maintenance of reactive sites responsible
for toxicity, and that these residues might also be involved as antigenic determinants in the formation of antibodies that are protective
and neutralizing to the toxin of C. botulinum.

This work was supported in part by the National Institutes
of Health, Grant #5-ROI-AI04180-05, and the National Science Foundation, Grant #GB-3057.

## References

Ambache, N., 1949, J. Physiol., 108, 127.

Andrews, P., 1965, Biochem. J., 96, 595.

Bonventre, P. F., and L. L. Kempe, 1960, J. Bacteriol., 79, 24.

Boroff, D. A., 1955, J. Bacteriol., 70, 363.

Boroff, D. A., and B. R. Das Gupta, 1966, Biochim. Biophys.
Acta, 117, 289.

Boroff, D. A., and B. R. Das Gupta, 1964, J. Biol. Chem.,
239, 3698.

Boroff, D. A., R. Townend, U. Fleck, and B. R. Das Gupta,
1966, J. Biol. Chem., 241, 5165.

Boroff, D. A., and M. Raynaud, 1952, J. Immunol., 68, 503.

Bouisset, L., J. Breuilland, and V. Grizov, 1957, Biol. Med.
(Paris), 151, 387.

Brooks, V. B., 1954, J. Physiol., 123, 501.

Buehler, H., E. Schantz, and C. Lamanna, 1947, J. Biol. Chem.,
169, 295.

Cann, J. R., and W. B. Goad, 1965, J. Biol. Chem., 240, 148.

Craven, G. R., E. Steers, Jr., and C. B. Anfinsen, 1965, J.
Biol. Chem., 240, 2468.

Crowle, A. J., 1962, Immunodiffusion, Academic Press, Inc.,
New York, p. 60.

Das Gupta, B. R., and D. A. Boroff, 1965, Biochim. Biophys.
Acta, 97, 157.

Das Gupta, B. R., D. A. Boroff, and E. Rothstein, 1966, Biochem. Biophys. Res. Commun., 22, 750.

Dickson, E. C., and C. Shevky, 1923, J. Exptl. Med., 37, 711.

Fraenkel-Conrat, M., B. A. Brandon, and M. Olcott, 1947, J.
Biol. Chem., 168, 99.

Freund, J., and M. V. Bonanto, 1944, J. Immunol., 48, 325.

Gendon, U. Z., 1957, J. Microbiol. Epidemiol. Immunol.
(U.S.S.R.), 3, 67.

Gerwing, J., C. E. Dolman, and H. S. Bains, 1965, J. Bacteriol.,
89, 1383.

Guyton, A. C., and M. A. MacDonald, 1947, Arch. Neurol.
Psychiat., 57, 578.

Koshland, D. E., V. D. Karkhanis, and M. G. Latham, 1964,
J. Amer. Chem. Soc., 86, 1448.

Lamanna, C., and J. P. Lowenthal, 1951, J. Bacteriol., 61, 751.

Lamanna, C., D. E. McElroy, and H. W. Eklund, 1946, Science,
103, 613.

Lowry, D. H., N. Rosebrough, A. L. Farr, and R. Randall,
1951, J. Biol. Chem., 193, 265.

Mager, J., S. H. Kindler, and N. Grossowicz, 1954, J. Gen. Microbiol., 10, 130.

Matveev, K. I., 1959, Botulism, Moscow State Publishers of Medical Literature, Moscow.

Moore, S., 1963, J. Biol. Chem., 238, 235.

Neumann, N. P., S. Moore, and W. M. Stein, 1962, Biochemistry, 1, 68.

Putnam, F. W., C. Lamanna, and D. G. Sharp, 1946, J. Biol. Chem., 165, 735.

Raynaud, M., and L. Second, 1949, Ann. Inst. Pasteur (Paris), 77, 316.

Schantz, E. J., and L. Spero, 1957, J. Amer. Chem. Soc., 79, 1623.

Schubel, K., 1921, Deutsch. Med. Wschr. (Stuttgart), 47, 1047.

Siegal. L. H., and K. J. Monty, 1965, Biochem. Biophys. Res. Commun., 19, 494.

Sluyterman, L. A., 1962, Biochim. Biophys. Acta, 60, 557.

Soroff, S., E. M. Young, R. A. McBride, and C. B. Coffey, 1966, Arch. Biochem., 113, 83.

Spies, J. R., and D. C. Chambers, 1949, Anal. Chem., 21, 1249.

von Hippel, P. H., and K. Y. Wong, 1964, Science, 145, 577.

Wagman, J., 1963, Arch. Biochem., 100, 414.

Weil, L., W. G. Gordon, and A. R. Buchart, 1951, Arch. Biochem., 33, 90.

Weil, L., S. James, and A. R. Buchart, 1951, Arch. Biochem., 34, 1.

Winbury, M. M., 1959, J. Physiol., 147, 1.

Yphantis, D. A., 1964, Biochemistry, 3, 297.

# THE BONGKREK TOXINS

A. G. van Veen
Graduate School of Nutrition
Cornell University
Ithaca, New York

## Introduction

In this paper, a review is given of research carried out in Indonesia prior to 1947 and later in Holland and elsewhere in connection with bongkrek poisonings. These poisonings had occurred for as long as could be remembered in Central Java (Indonesia), mainly in the province of Banjumas and its surrounding areas. This region is inhabited by many millions of people, mostly small farmers. Rice is produced as one of the main staples in the plains of the province; coconut groves can be found everywhere in the lowlands and form the basis of a village or cottage industry.

Although mass poisonings involving sometimes as many as 200 people had been known to occur since at least the end of the last century, the cause was unknown; it was certain only that it was not a contagious disease. It was extremely difficult to obtain any remnants of food that might be suspected as the cause because, after an outbreak, the population usually threw all food away so as not to be bothered by inquiries and investigations. Moreover, the population held the belief that the poisonings were due to evil spirits or to the Goddess of the Indian Ocean in an angry mood!

The poisonings occurred a few times a year, and there were never many survivors. The characteristic signs and symptoms were not well known because the poisonings were usually reported only after most victims had died. However, severe spasms and unconsciousness seemed to be common features.

During the economic depression in Indonesia, between 1931 and 1937, the poisonings were very numerous. Mertens and van Veen from the Eijkman Institute in Djakarta began investigation of them.

## Microbiological Research

Fermented products such as soybeans, peanut press cake, and coconut press cake that have been treated with fungi are very

43

popular in great parts of Indonesia; their manufacture constitutes
a village or cottage industry. In general, these fermented products are much more acceptable than the original foods; they are
easier to prepare for consumption and are more digestible. However, the techniques of fermentation under simple conditions are
not as simple as might be thought.

Van Veen and Mertens (1934, 1933) were able to obtain a small
quantity of a poorly fermented coconut product suspected to be
the cause of a poisoning in which most people died; an emulsion
of it proved fatal to a monkey and to white rats after feeding by
stomach tube.

It was found that as a rule the poisonous products were poorly
fermented and that they always contained coconut press cake (the
fermented product is then called "bongkrek" or "tempeh bongkrek")
or grated coconut ("semaji"). A few grams of the poisonous material, even after having been cooked in a soup or fried in oil,
seemed to be enough to kill a man.

It was finally possible to isolate from the abundance of fungi,
bacteria, and yeasts a bacterium that appeared to be responsible
for the toxicity. It was named Pseudomonas cocovenenans. Depending on the type of culture medium, the bacterium grows in
different forms resembling micrococci, vibrios, or mycelium-
like threads, and in colonies of different forms (rough and smooth),
and different colors (deep yellow to white). Neither the form of
the colonies or of the bacterium, nor the pigmentation appeared
to be stable characteristic properties of definite strains; the
prevalent form of the colony or of the bacterium itself depends
on the culture medium and other conditions.

Especially on glycerol-containing media, the colonies often,
but not always, show a bright yellow color; on glucose media and
media containing the fatty acids from coconut oil, the pigmentation is usually far less.

It appeared that the villagers who were used to manufacturing
bongkrek or semaji for themselves or for sale nearly always
produced good, harmless products, that is, products that were
completely fermented, covered by, and penetrated by the fungus.
The fungus is a Rhizopus, probably the same as used for manufacturing tempeh kedelee from soybeans, namely, Rhizopus oli-
gosporus. The fermentation results in a white cake, one-half
to one inch thick.

However, in periods of economic distress when the villagers
who customarily sell their coconuts, copra, or coconut press
cake to the processers cannot do so, they start to manufacture
bongkrek or semaji themselves for home consumption. Many of
them, not knowing the technique, may not be able to get a good
fermentation, so that the Rhizopus does not grow fast enough
(e.g., within 18 to 48 hours) and other microorganisms get an

opportunity to grow. In most cases, these will be mainly spoilage
bacteria or other fungi but every now and then there may be an
accidental infection with the toxic P. cocovenenans, and this mi-
croorganism may be able to multiply fast for two reasons. Usually the fungus grows much faster than any bacteria or yeast present
in the basic material, but if it does not do so the Pseudomonas has
a chance. The latter, moreover, excretes two antibiotic substances which inhibit any fungus growth that takes place. Later
van Veen (1950) was able to show that at least one of the substances causing the fatal poisoning in man is also a strong antibiotic for the Rhizopus.

In spite of their endeavors, van Veen and Mertens were not
able to isolate P. cocovenenans from soil, water, coconut shells,
etc., in the province of Banjumas. But, of course, in a tropical,
humid environment it is difficult to isolate a bacterium unless one
has at one's disposal a very efficient and specific enrichment
procedure.

Van Veen and Mertens inoculated other foodstuffs that are commonly fermented in Indonesia, such as soybeans and peanut press
cake, under the usual fermentation conditions with P. cocovenenans.
No toxicity could be observed. The reason has not yet been fully
investigated.

## Toxicological and Chemical Research

The authors were able to extract from suitable culture media
two poisonous substances. One was the yellow pigment already
mentioned, soluble in water and chloroform, and heat stable.
The other poison appeared to be a substance having the characteristics of an unsaturated fatty acid, heat stable in oil solution (and
also in alkaline, aqueous solution) but extremely unstable when
purified. The stability of both poisons at high temperatures in a
fat emulsion explains the high toxicity of fried bongkrek, of which
only a few grams may be fatal.

For the investigations on toxicity, white rats, pigeons, rabbits,
and sometimes monkeys (van Veen and Mertens, 1936; van Veen
and Mertens, 1935) were used.

Some characteristics of the two poisonous substances are described now.

a. Toxoflavin. The yellow poison was called toxoflavin because
its chemical and physical properties were very similar to those of
riboflavin, which at that time had only recently been discovered.
For example, it had a yellow color, showed green (though weak)
fluorescence, was stable against oxidants, and had an absorption
spectrum somewhat similar to that of riboflavin.

Toxoflavin could be produced relatively easily by cultivating the
bacterium in an aqueous glycerol-containing culture medium, which
also contained peptone and salts, exposed to air in a thin layer at
30°C.

For its isolation, toxoflavin was extracted with chloroform after adding anhydrous sodium sulfate. After purification it crystallized into beautiful yellow flat needles, having a melting point of 171°C. It is discolored by sulfur dioxide, but after shaking with air the yellow color returns. It is very stable against hydrogen peroxide and bromine. Five to 10 μg injected into a rat kills the animal within an hour (Darwis and Grevenstuk, 1935). However, when given orally the pure substance was not very toxic for rats or monkeys. One to 2 mg orally caused dizziness and sleepiness in a monkey of about 1 kg, but the animal usually recovered in about 12 hours.

According to the first analysis, the empirical formula was $C_6H_6N_4O_2$, and there was at least one N-methyl group. Treated with $KClO_3$ and HCl, the substance gave a strong murexide reaction and methylalloxan was one of the oxidation products (Stern, 1935). The authors thought the substance to be an isomer of methylxanthin but later on Berends and co-workers (van Damme et al., 1960) showed that the Indonesian microanalyses had not been right and that the empirical formula was $C_7H_7N_5O_2$ containing two 6-membered rings, a pyrimidine and a triazine system, both with one N-methyl group. Their hypothesis was confirmed by Daves and co-workers (1962), who were able to synthesize toxoflavin with the following formula:

The biosynthetic pathway was recently investigated by Levenberg and Linton (1966).

Berends and co-workers also investigated the cause of the toxicity of toxoflavin (Latuasan and Berends, 1961). They investigated the action of toxoflavin on yeasts and some other microorganisms, such as E. coli, Shigella, Proteus vulgaris, and B. subtilis. They found that toxoflavin acts as an electron carrier, which makes it possible to by-pass the cytochrome system. The final result is the production of hydrogen peroxide; this may explain the strong antibiotic and poisonous character of toxoflavin. Its inactivity under anaerobic conditions is in line with this finding.

b.  Bongkrek Acid.  The second poison was called, by the original investigators, bongkrek acid, a substance with all the characteristics of a highly unsaturated fatty acid.  It can be separated easily from toxoflavin because the free acid is soluble in the usual fat solvents but is not soluble in water.  When shaken with aqueous sodium carbonate, however, it dissolves easily in the aqueous phase.

Bongkrek acid is very stable when dissolved in coconut oil (e. g., as in bongkrek or in semaji) and in alkaline solution; but the free acid becomes extremely unstable the more it is purified, and it is difficult to free it from some of the fatty acids in the coconut-oil-containing culture medium during purification.  One to 1.5 mg of the not quite pure material in the form of its sodium salt is usually fatal when given orally to a 1 to 2 kg monkey (van Veen and Mertens, 1936;  van Veen and Mertens, 1935).

In general, bongkrek acid is a much more severe poison for animals and humans than is toxoflavin.  It mobilizes the glycogen from the liver, thus leading to a hyperglycemia, that is followed by a fatal hypoglycemia.  Usually severe spasms set in;  these are typical for the clinical picture of bongkrek poisonings in both human beings and experimental animals.  The injection of glucose restores the blood sugar level and prolongs life, but it was found that it does not restore liver glycogen, and human lives could not be saved by such injections.  On the other hand, tissue glycogen is only partly affected (van Veen and Mertens, 1936;  van Veen and Mertens, 1935).

For experimental purposes, bongkrek acid can be produced easily by cultivating the bacterium on partly defatted grated coconut.

Van Veen and Mertens found that the pharmacological activity could be measured rather easily by the optical activity.  For example, an impure preparation, of which 2 mg given orally were lethal for a pigeon, showed a specific rotation $[\alpha]_D^{28} = 100$ to $115°C$ as sodium salt in an alcohol solution.

They were able to purify bongkrek acid partly through preparation of its silver salt and partly by column chromatography, but the purer the substance became the easier it was inactivated.  Their purest preparation still contained some of the lower fatty acids from coconut oil and showed an average composition of about $(C_{11}H_{16}O_3)x$; it was highly unsaturated.

After the war, when antibiotics had become known, van Veen found that bongkrek acid in salt form was a very active antibiotic for the bongkrek fungus, Rhizopus, as well as for Penicillium glaucum, yeast, and a number of bacteria (van Veen, 1950).  It appeared to act in the same way on these microorganisms as it did on humans and experimental animals; that is, to interfere with carbohydrate metabolism.

Research on this interesting substance was later resumed by
Nugteren and Berends (1957). They improved the isolation method
by making use of a chromatopile. However, they were also unable to obtain crystalline derivatives. They came to the conclusion that bongkrek acid has the empirical formula $C_{29}H_{40}O_7$ and
that it is a highly unsaturated tricarboxylic acid with seven double
bonds (with at least two conjugated systems). They further concluded that it is branched and contains a tertiary methoxyl group
and has a specific rotation of $[\alpha] = 165°C$ in a 2% aqueous sodium
bicarbonate solution.

Berends and co-workers also investigated the method of action
of bongkrek acid (Welling et al., 1960). They showed that it interferes with the citric acid cycle in heart muscle tissue. It was
found that the oxidation of pyruvate, $\alpha$-ketoglutarate, and malate
was inhibited, whereas the oxidation of succinate and $\beta$-hydroxy-
butyrate was stimulated. The phosphorylation coupled with these
oxidations proved to be even more sensitive to bongkrek acid. The
concentration required to produce these effects on isolated mitochondria is very low; in most cases $10^{-6}$ M is very effective.

Bongkrek and semaji are cheap and attractive foods and, as far
as is known, bongkrek poisonings still occur.

One interesting practical experiment has been done by a former
co-worker, Mr. Harsono Hardjohutomo (oral communication to
van Veen).

When the coconut-containing material before inoculation with the
fungus is slightly acidified (e. g., about pH 5.5), the Pseudomonas
scarcely grows, but the fungus does. He proposed that the material be mixed with the acid-containing leaves of an Oxalis species
that grows everywhere as a weed in Banjumas. He was able to
show in laboratory experiments that in this way, after inoculation
with both P. cocovenenans and Rhizopus, the material does not become toxic. However, Oxalis leaves are an unusual ingredient
for the population; moreover, they seem to give the material an
unusual dark color that may explain why the population has, as
far as known, not made use of this simple safety measure.

Summary

A review is given of the investigations of bongkrek poisonings
of Central Java (Indonesia) which have not been reported from
other parts of Indonesia or from other countries. These poisonings attracted attention because of the clinical picture, the high
mortality rate, and also because the cause of them was unknown.
Investigations were started during the economic depression period
in the 1930's, when mass poisonings were relatively numerous
(e.g., up to 10 or 12 a year).

It was found that toxic substances were sometimes present in
poorly fermented coconut products, fermented with the help of a

fungus of the Rhizopus species. The poor fermentation appeared
to be due in part to poor techniques, but even more to the action
of a contaminating bacterium named by the investigators Pseudomonas cocovenenans. This bacterium produces two substances,
named toxoflavin and bongkrek acid, which both have antibiotic
properties. It was found that bongkrek acid seemed to act in the
same way in microorganisms, experimental animals, and humans,
that is, to interfere with carbohydrate metabolism. It was not
possible to isolate this bacterium from soil, water, or other foods
in Central Java. The bacterium seems able to produce poisonous
substances only in coconut products, not in soybeans or peanut
press cake, which (after fermentation) are also very popular foods
in this region.

Under ordinary conditions, both antibiotics are quite stable;
this explains why sometimes even a few grams of the fried toxic
material may be lethal for humans. The chemical structure and
physiological action of the two toxic substances are described, as
well as the clinical symptoms resulting from their ingestion.

## References

Darwis, A., and A. Grevenstuk, 1935, Geneesk. T. v. Ned.
Indie, 75. 104.

Daves, G. D., R. K. Robins, and C. C. Cheng, 1962, J. Amer.
Chem. Soc., 84, 1724.

Latuasan, H. E., and W. Berends, 1961, Biochim. Biophys.
Acta, 52, 502.

Levenberg, B., and S. N. Linton, 1966, J. Biol. Chem., 241,
846.

Nugteren, D. H., and W. Berends, 1957, Rec. Trav. Chim.
Pays Bas, 76, 13.

Stern, K. G., 1935, Biochem. J., 21, 500.

Van Damme, P. A., A. G. Johannes, H. C. Cox, and W. Berends,
1960, Rec. Trav. Chim. Pays Bas, 79, 255.

van Veen, A. G., 1950, Doc. Neerl. Indon. Morbis Tropicis, 2,
185.

van Veen, A. G., and W. K. Mertens, 1933, Geneesk. T. v.
Ned. Indie, 73, 1223.

van Veen, A. G., and W. K. Mertens, 1934, Rec. Trav. Chim.
Bas, 53, 257.

van Veen, A. G., and W. K. Mertens, 1935, Geneesk. T. v.
Ned. Indie, 75, 1059.

van Veen, A. G., and W. K. Mertens, 1936, Arch. Neerl. Physiol., 11, 73.

Welling, J., J. A. Cohen, and W. Berends, 1960, Biochem. Pharmacol., 3, 122.

# BIOCHEMICAL STUDIES ON CERTAIN ALGAL TOXINS

Edward J. Schantz
U.S. Army Biological Center
Fort Detrick, Frederick, Maryland

## Identification and Location of Toxic Algae

For the past 200 years medical records from various parts of the world have documented fatal cases of food poisoning in humans from eating various types of shellfish. Captain Cook's expeditions and those of Captain Vancouver along the Pacific coast of North America had many deaths and much sickness of the crew from eating mussels and clams from this area. The Russian expeditions in Alaska and to the south along the Pacific coast experienced similar difficulties. In 1885 an unusually large outbreak of poisonings occurred near Wilhelmshaven, Germany, killing many people who had eaten mussels picked from the shores of the North Sea. This outbreak stimulated many investigations on the cause of the poison occurring in the mussels, but little success was attained because of the rapid disappearance of the poison in the shellfish after such unexpected and sporadic occurrences. Many theories were proposed to explain the phenomenon, such as infections of the shellfish with bacteria, concentration of certain metallic salts in the shellfish at certain times, and the like. The solution to this problem came about 50 years later during several serious outbreaks of poisoning that occurred along the California coast during the period 1928 to 1937. During this period, Sommer, Meyer, Kofoid, Wedon, and their associates at the University of California (Sommer and Meyer, 1937; Sommer et al., 1937) discovered that the toxicity of the mussels correlated with the occurrence of a particular marine alga in the water upon which the mussels fed. This organism was identified as one of the dinoflagellates, Gony-aulax catenella. Sommer collected the organisms from the ocean and found that extracts of these organisms would kill mice as readily as extracts of the mussels. He also placed mussels in tanks containing a unialgal culture of G. catenella and found that the mussels became very toxic, thus proving unequivocally that the poison in the mussels resulted from feeding on this organism.

Blooms producing a red tide of G. catenella in nature become apparent when the number of organisms reaches 20,000 to 30,000 or

more per ml, but mussels may become too toxic for human consumption when the number has reached around 200 per ml.  When
a bloom of G. catenella, which lasts about 2 weeks, recedes to a
sufficiently low level, the toxicity of the mussels soon disappears.
California mussels (Mytilus californianus) and bay mussels (Mytil-
lus edulis) bind the poison in the dark gland or hepatopancreas
when feeding on large numbers of G. catenella.  Apparently under
these circumstances they are excreting or destroying the poison
more slowly than the poison accumulates.  When the number of
organisms becomes sufficiently low (<200/ml) the rate of destruction overtakes the accumulation, and within 2 or 3 weeks the mussels are again safe for human consumption.  In contrast, the Alaska
butter clam (Saxidomas giganteus) binds in the siphon a poison that
is identical to that isolated from mussels; it is held for a year or
more without appreciable destruction or excretion.  This species
of clam is believed to become quite toxic from even an extremely
low number of G. catenella in the water.  Human poisoning from
eating toxic shellfish has occurred in many places throughout the
world, mainly in the areas around the North Sea, the Bay of Fundy,
and along the coasts of South Africa, California, British Columbia,
south and southeastern Alaska, and Japan.  Symptoms of poisoning may begin about 30 minutes after toxic mussels are consumed,
with a tingling sensation in the lips and finger tips followed by a
progressive paralysis and death in 3 to 20 hours, depending upon
the dose.  If one survives 24 hours, the prognosis is good.  The
medical aspects of poisoning in man are described by Meyer
(1953).

The work of Sommer et al. (1937) was the first to demonstrate
the presence of a poison in G. catenella and to establish a definite
relationship between this alga and the occurrence of a poison in
the California mussels that causes paralysis and death in man and
animals.  Subsequently, the poison in scallops from the Bay of
Fundy was associated with the occurrence of G. tamarensis Lebour
(Needler, 1949; Prakash, 1963), and the poison in the Belgian
mussels in the North Sea with the occurrence of Pyrodinium phoneu
(Woloszynska and Conrad, 1939; Koch, 1939).  The source of the
poison in Alaska butter clams is not definitely known, but G. catenella may be involved (Schantz and Magnusson, 1964).  Connell
and Cross (1950) and Gates and Wilson (1960) have implicated G.
monilata Howell in the mortality of fish in the Gulf of Mexico during
red tide blooms.  Schradie and Bliss (1962) have reported that G.
polyedra Stein produces a poison that in some respects appears
similar to that produced by G. catenella.

In addition to species of Gonyaulax, other dinoflagellates that have
been implicated in toxin production are Gymnodinium veneficum
and Gymnodinium brevi Davis.  Abbott and Ballantine (1957) have
demonstrated the presence of a toxin in unialgal cultures of G.

veneficum that is toxic to fish and higher animals.  The great
fish kills along the Gulf Coast of Florida caused by red tides of
G. brevi are believed to be due to a toxin produced by this organism (Ray and Wilson, 1957).

Other algae have caused public health problems and heavy economic damage by killing domestic animals and destroying fish
populations.  Several species of blue-green algae, particularly
Anabaena flos-aquae and Microcystis aeruginosa, have produced
blooms in shallow fresh-water lakes throughout the world that
have killed thousands of cattle, horses, sheep, hogs, certain
fowl, and dogs that drank water containing large numbers of these
organisms.  The occurrence of the poisons is sporadic even within one particular species.  Concentrations usually become high on
the leeward side of fresh-water lakes after heavy algal growths in
shallow water.  Such occurrences have been reported in North
America, particularly from North and South Dakota, Minnesota,
Iowa, Wisconsin, Illinois, and Michigan in the United States and
from the Canadian provinces of Alberta, Saskatchewan, Manitoba,
and Ontario (Grant and Hughes, 1953).  The occurrence of toxic
blooms in these areas has been studied by several investigators
in the United States and Canada and recently reviewed by Gorham
(1960).  The occurrence is similar to that reported in Russia,
Argentina, Brazil, Australia, South Africa, and other countries.
Other species of blue-green algae have been implicated in poisoning of livestock, but the occurrence of these poisonings is rare
compared with the previous two (Gorham, 1960).

Several investigators in Israel (Otterstrom and Steeman-Nielsen,
1939; Reich and Aschner, 1947; Shilo and Rosenberger, 1964; and
Parnas, 1963) have investigated the phytoflagellate (golden-brown
alga) Prymnesium parvum Carter.  This organism produces various toxic principles, including a highly potent ichthyotoxin termed
prymnesin, that has caused high mortality of fish in brackish water ponds and estuarine water.  Fish kills due to this organism in
regions where carp are raised commercially in ponds have resulted in great economic losses.  Other flagellates of this order,
Ochromonas danica and O. malhamensis, also produce poisons
that are active against fish but in a different manner than prymnesin (Reich and Spiegelstein, 1964).

In addition to the toxic algae listed, others have been reported
throughout the torrid and temperate zones of the world, but little
is known about their toxic nature (Ballentine and Abbott, 1957).
Some algae are toxic to humans because of allergenic reactions
(Heise, 1949 and 1951), and still others that produce toxins in water purification systems may cause outbreaks of gastroenteritis
(Tisdale, 1931).  It is the purpose of this paper, however, to point
out the important algal toxins and to describe the biochemical properties of those that have been isolated and characterized.  A sum-

mation of the occurrence and properties of the important toxic
algae is presented in Table 1.

## Isolation and Characterization of Toxin from Algae

Of the several poisons and toxins that have been identified in
algal cultures, only two have been isolated in pure form and
characterized chemically and physically. The first of these was
the so-called "fast death factor" (FDF) found in certain unialgal
cultures of the blue-green alga M. aeruginosa reported by Bishop
et al. (1959) of the National Research Council, Canada, in 1959.
These workers termed the toxin the "fast death factor" because
a minimum lethal dose by intraperitoneal injection killed mice
in 30 to 60 minutes in contrast to another toxin found in these
preparations that caused death in 4 to 48 hours. This they called
the "slow death factor (SDF)." After considerable effort in se-
lecting strains, a unialgal culture of M. aeruginosa, designated
NRC-1, was obtained that produced the FDF and SDF in quantities
equal to those of the natural state but with the advantages of having
control of the critical factors for toxin production. Thus these
investigators were able to produce a continuous laboratory bloom
on a scale sufficient to yield 1 to 2 kg of freeze-dried cells per
month. The medium was composed of demineralized water with
0.04% $NaNO_3$ as a nitrogen source plus various inorganic salts
and citrate as described by Hughes et al. (1958). Cultures were
illuminated and held at 25°C for 4 days for maximum toxin production. The algal cells were agglomerated with a small amount of
aluminum sulfate and HCl to permit rapid centrifugation. Fresh
cells were not toxic to mice but became toxic when they were frozen
and thawed, sonic-disintegrated, or decomposed by semianaerobic
incubation. The toxin (FDF) was extracted from the decomposed
algal cells with water and subjected to electrophoresis on paper,
first under acidic conditions and then under alkaline conditions,
yielding a highly purified toxic component that killed mice at a
minimum lethal dose of about 9 µg in a 20-gram mouse, or 450 µg
per kg. It is a moderately toxic substance. Its specific toxicity
in terms of minimum lethal mouse doses per gram of solids is
$1.1 \times 10^5$. Because the FDF formed only on the decomposition of
the algal cells, it is believed to be an endotoxin. It was found to
be a polypeptide made up of 10 amino acid units as follows: one
unit each of L-aspartic acid, D-serine, L-valine, and L-ornithine
and two units each of L-glutamic acid, L-alanine, and L-leucine.
The molecular weight is about 1200. The occurrence of the un-
natural amino acid D-serine in the peptide is interesting. The
toxin did not react with reagents for terminal amino acids of proteins, so it was assumed that the peptide must be cyclic. The
amino acid sequence and structure have not yet been determined.

Table 1.  Toxins Produced by Various Algae

Pyrophyta; Dinoflagellates

| Species | Common Location | Action of Toxin | Characteristics |
|---|---|---|---|
| Gonyaulax catenella | Pacific coast of North America | Toxic to all higher animals. Predators bind toxin. Poison blocks sodium influx in nerve cells. | Among most potent poisons. Low mol wt (372). Water-soluble purine. Structure reported. |
| Gonyaulax tamarensis | North American Atlantic coast | Appears similar to G. catenella poison. | Appears similar to G. catenella poison. |
| Gonyaulax polyedra | California coast | Toxic to mice and fish. | Somewhat similar to G. catenella poison. |
| Gonyaulax monilata | Gulf of Mexico | Toxic to fish. | Not characterized. |
| Gymnodinium veneficum | Isolated from the English Channel | Toxic to fish and mice. | High molecular weight. Water soluble. |
| Gymnodinium brevi | Gulf of Mexico | Toxic to fish. | Not characterized. |

Cyanophyta; Blue-Green Algae

| | | | |
|---|---|---|---|
| Microcystis aeruginosa | Shallow fresh water lakes | Toxic to many animals. (FDF) | Cyclic polypeptide of 10 amino acid units. Mol wt about 1200. Water soluble. |
| Anabaena flos-aquae | Shallow fresh water lakes | Toxic to many animals. Kills faster than M. aeruginosa. (VFDF) | Water soluble. |

Chrysophyta; Yellow-Brown Algae; Phytoflagellates

| | | | |
|---|---|---|---|
| Pyrmnesium parvum | Brackish water ponds and estuarine water. | Toxic to fish and all gill-breathing animals. Potent hemolytic agent. | Water soluble. Non-dialyzable thermo-labile. May be a saponinlike compound. |

The "slow death factor" associated with the algal cultures is believed to result from the decomposition of the bacteria in the culture, and its presence could be demonstrated by differential centrifugation of the algae from the bacteria and allowing decomposition to take place. The decomposed algal cells yielded the FDF; the bacterial cells yielded the SDF.

The poison produced by Anabaena flos-aquae acts even more rapidly than the FDF and was termed by the Canadian workers the "very fast death factor" (VFDF). However, this toxin has been obtained only from natural cultures and has not been isolated or characterized. It is water soluble and probably lower in molecular weight than the FDF (Gorham, 1960).

The other algal toxin that has been isolated and characterized is that produced by Gonyaulax catenella, recently reported by Schantz et al. (1966). Although mussel poison has been thoroughly characterized (Schantz et al., 1957; Mold et al., 1957; Rapoport et al., 1964) and the relationship between it and G. catenella definitely established, one could not assume that the poison from the two sources was the same. There was a question about changes in the poison that might have occurred by passing through the shellfish and also a question regarding the production and structure of the poison through a possible symbiotic effect of the bacteria associated with this dinoflagellate. Answers to these questions have been sought by several investigators.

Riegel et al. (1949) obtained concentrates of the poison from G. catenella collected from the Pacific Ocean off the California coast and found that many properties of the poison in crude extracts were similar to those of the poison from mussels. Burke et al. (1960) have studied the chromatographic behavior of crude extracts of G. catenella cells from axenic culture and found the poison to chromatograph similarly to mussel poison.

For the studies at the U.S. Army Biological Center, a unialgal bacteria-free culture of G. catenella was obtained from Dr. L. Provasoli of the Haskins Laboratory. Using this culture in a sterile medium made up of sea water collected near Ocean City, Maryland, with addition of 100 mg of $KNO_3$, 10 mg of $K_2HPO$, 1 mg $FeCl_3$, and 0.05 mg of $Na_2SiO_3$ per liter with the pH at 8.6, we were successful in producing over 200 mg of the poison. Culturing was carried out in 2-liter Fernbach flasks containing 1 liter of the medium at 13 to 15°C for about 17 days. At that time, the cell count usually reached 20,000 to 30,000 per ml and the bioassay was 2 to 3 mouse units per ml when the poison was extracted from the cells. The cells were filtered from the medium and the poison was extracted from the cells on the filter paper with weak hydrochloric acid at pH 2 to 3.

The poison was purified by chromatography on a carboxylic acid exchange resin, Amberlite XE-64, followed by chromatog-

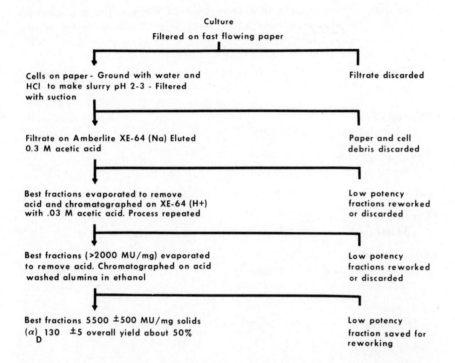

Fig. 1.  Scheme for purification of <u>Gonyaulax catenella</u> poison.

raphy on acid-washed alumina as illustrated in Figure 1.  Details of the purification have been published elsewhere (Schantz
et al., 1966).  The method of purification turned out to be almost
identical to that we used for the purification of the poison from
toxic mussels and clams.  This fact was evidence of the similarity of the G. catenella poison to clam and mussel poisons.  The
poison is a rapidly acting, highly toxic nitrogenous base.  A mouse
unit (MU), defined as the minimum amount to kill a 20-gram mouse
in 15 minutes (Sommer and Meyer, 1937; Schantz et al., 1958), is
0.2 μg or 10 μg per kg.  Mice that do not die from a dose in 15 minutes usually will recover.  The lethal dose of shellfish poison by
intravenous injection for rabbits is 3 to 4 μg per kg of body weight.
Data collected in connection with accidental cases of poisoning in
humans indicate that the oral dose may be less than a mg.  Table 2
shows several properties of G. catenella poison compared with
those of clam and mussel poisons.  The specific toxicity of the
poison in terms of MU per gram of solids is $5.1 \times 10^6$.  The poison
is a white hygroscopic solid with a specific optical rotation of +128°,
possesses two basic titratable groups, $pK_a$ at 8.2 and 11.5, shows
no absorption in the ultraviolet (220-360 mμ), and is easily reduced to a nontoxic substance with the uptake of 1 mole of hydrogen.

Table 2.  Comparison of Properties of Poison from Cultured
Gonyaulax catenella Cells with Poison from Mussels and Clams

| Property | Clam Poison | Mussel Poison | G. catenella Poison |
|---|---|---|---|
| Bioassay (MU/mg)[a] | 5200 | 5300 | 5100 |
| Specific optical rotation | +128° | +130° | +128° |
| pK$_a$ | 8.3; 11.5 | 8.3; 11.5 | 8.2; 11.5 |
| Diffusion coefficient | $4.9 \times 10^{-6}$ | $4.9 \times 10^{-6}$ | $4.8 \times 10^{-6}$ |
| Absorption in ultraviolet and visible[b] | None | None | None |
| N content (Kjeldahl) | 26.8 | 26.1 | 26.3 |
| Sakaguchi[c] | - | - | - |
| Benedict-Behre[c] | + | + | + |
| Jaffe[c] | + | + | + |
| Reduction with H$_2$ | Dihydro derivative, nontoxic | Dihydro derivative, nontoxic | Dihydro derivative, nontoxic |

[a]All bioassay values are within experimental error of the value
5500 ± 500 MU/mg solids reported previously for clam and
mussel poisons (Schantz et al., 1958).

[b]Infrared absorption of G. catenella poison was identical with
that of clam and mussel poisons.  See Figure 2.

[c]Tests carried out as described by Mold et al. (1957).

Courtesy Am. Chem. Soc., Biochemistry, 5, 1191 (1966).

It gives a positive Jaffe and Benedict-Behre test, but after reduction to a nontoxic substance these tests are negative.  The molecular formula of the dihydrochloride salt is $C_{10}H_{17}N_7O_4 \cdot 2HCl$ with
a molecular weight of 372.  All chemical and biological properties
and physical measurements on G. catenella poison were identical
(within experimental error) to those obtained on mussel and clam
poisons.  The infrared spectra of G. catenella and mussel poisons
are shown in Figure 2.  Rechromatography of the poison in the

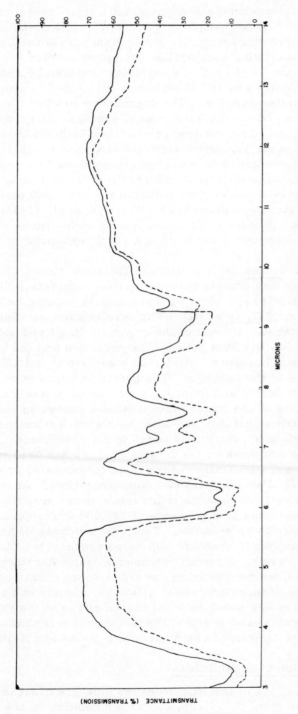

Fig. 2.  Infrared spectra of purified G. catenella poison (solid line) and purified mussel poison (broken line).  The break in the curves at 9.3 μ is caused by a change from one photo-cell to another for the longer wave lengths.  Courtesy Am. Chem. Soc., Biochemistry, 5, 1191 (1966).

highly toxic fractions on the alumina did not significantly increase the specific toxicity or change the specific rotation of the poison.

In a cooperative study with Dr. Henry Rapoport at the University of California, a similar comparison was made between various degradation products of each of the poisons obtained by reduction with hydrogen iodide and red phosphorus and oxidation with hydrogen peroxide in alkaline solution. The degradation products from G. catenella poison showed the same n.m.r. spectra, infrared and ultra violet spectra, the same melting points taken individually and when mixed with the same derivative from the clam and mussel poisons, and the same $R_f$ values upon being chromatographed on paper.

These results constitute good evidence that the chemical structure of G. catenella is identical to that of the clam and mussel poisons. The structure proposed by Rapoport et al. (1964) shows that clam poison (Saxitoxin) is a purine base with a three-carbon bridge linking positions 3 and 9 and a methyl carbamate at position 6.

The fact that G. catenella poison has the same chemical structure as the clam and mussel poisons verifies completely the work of Sommer et al. (1937), showing that mussels become toxic from the consumption of G. catenella. The results point out that the poison is a metabolic product of the organism itself and not a result of any symbiotic effect between the organism and the bacteria associated with it in nature. Also, the structure is not affected by the presence of the bacteria. The poison is bound in and released from the dark gland or hepatopancreas of mussels and probably in the siphon of the butter clam without a change in structure. This binding action probably protects the shellfish from the poison, but the mechanism by which it is bound is not understood.

Considerable progress by the Israeli workers has been made on the production and purification of the toxin (prymnesin) produced by P. parvum (I. Parnas, personal communication). At least two chemically distinct components still remain in the purified preparations. These toxins probably exceed 100,000 in molecular weight and do not appear to be proteins. They give evidence of being saponinlike compounds that are high in polysacharides (Reich et al., 1965; Z. Paster, personal communication). Recent improvements in techniques for culturing the organism in axenic culture using a medium of inorganic salts, vitamins, alanine and glycerol instead of diluted sea water have increased yields of the toxins needed for chemical and physical characterization (Rahat and Jahn, 1965; Z. Paster, personal communication; Rahat and Reich, 1963).

## Biological Action of Algal Toxins

With the exception of the FDF from the blue-green algae and possibly the poison from G. catenella, our information on the physiological effects and mechanism of action of algal toxins has been ob-

tained on crude extracts. This means that other substances present in the preparations may have a qualifying effect on the observations.

As observed in Table 1, some of the toxins are effective against
fish but not higher animals, whereas others are toxic to a variety
of animals. The highly potent poison in G. catenella does not kill
mussels and clams and, as far as we know, does not disturb their
normal physiological function or feeding habits. However, the toxin
produced by G. veneficum (Abbott and Ballantine, 1957) will cause
bivalves to close and stop feeding and eventually will kill mussels
that do not close completely in the cultures of this organism. Animals of the group Polychaeta such as Arenicola marino are completely unaffected by G. veneficum toxin. Mice are killed by injection of the toxin. The specific action is believed to be due to a
depolarization of nerve cells. G. catenella poison is lethal to all
higher animals when administered orally or by injection and to
frogs and fish by injection. As far as I know, no one has tried injecting this poison into the circulatory system of a mussel in its
natural habitat. The fact that shellfish feed on G. catenella poison,
which is a low-molecular-weight substance and readily dialyzable,
indicates that the protective mechanism mentioned earlier must be
a very efficient one and should be an interesting subject for further
study. A 50-gram mussel in nature with a hepatopancreas weighing
about 1 gram will bind 50,000 mouse units or about 9 mg of poison,
but freshly sliced or ground hepatopancreas from mussels will not
bind poison.

The toxin of the blue-green fresh water alga, M. aeruginosa,
(FDF) studied by the Canadians (Bishop et al., 1959; Gorham,
1960) is toxic to a great variety of animals except waterfowl, in-
dicating that the waterfowl have a mechanism to protect them against
the toxin. In most animals, the FDF produces pallor followed by
violent convulsions, prostration, and death. Upon autopsy, the
liver has a mottled appearance caused by cellular breakdown. On
the other hand, the toxin from Anabaena flos-aquae (VFDF) will kill
waterfowl (Gorham, 1960). As mentioned previously, the latter
toxin kills mice very rapidly, with death preceded by paralysis,
tremors, and mild convulsions. Upon autopsy, the liver appears
normal. It is apparent, therefore, that these two toxins must be
different in their chemical structure. The FDF has no antigenic
activity and no antibiotic activity, although its structure as a cyclic
polypeptide would suggest this possibility.

The specific action of the toxins from the brown alga P. parvum
have been studied quite extensively, even though the toxin has not
been isolated in pure form (Shilo and Rosenberger, 1960; Parnas
et al., 1962; Ulitzer and Shilo, 1966; Yariv and Hestrin, 1961;
Parnas and Abbott, 1965). The ichthyotoxin inhibits the transfer of
oxygen across the gill membranes of fish and is toxic to almost all

gill-breathing fish, molluscs, and arthropods and to gill-breathing stages of amphibia.

The toxin also causes hemolysis of red blood cells and an anti-spasmodic effect on guinea pig ileum. The ichthyotoxic and hemolytic effects appear to be associated with one substance, while the antispasmodic effect appears to be associated with another substance. Irradiation with visible and ultraviolet light, heating at 37°C, and treatment at high pH caused a rapid decline in the latter effect while the ichthyotoxic and hemolytic effects decreased slowly and at the same rate. Spiegelstein (personal communication) has found that the Ochromonas toxins are similar in activity to the toxins from P. parvum but differ quantitatively and may have different structures.

Because of the identical chemical structure, it is assumed that G. catenella poison should have the same physiological action in animals as mussel and clam poisons. Studies on the action of G. catenella poison have been initiated but not reported. However, in the case of mussel poison, it has been shown that propagation of impulses in nerves and skeletal muscles is blocked without any de-polarization (Evans, 1964; Kao and Nishiyama, 1965a; Dettbarn et al., 1965; H. Grundfest, 1965, personal communication). Kao and Nishiyama (1965b) have further shown that the block is due to some specific interference with the increase in sodium permeability normally associated with excitation. The resting membrane conductances attributed chiefly to potassium and chloride permeabilities are unaffected. The action is similar to that observed for tetrodotoxin and tarichatoxin (Kao and Nishiyama, 1965b; Kao and Fuhrman, 1963; Nakamura et al., 1965).

The shellfish poisons are among the most potent substances known to man, and at the present time no effective antidote against them is known. The poisons are not antigenic, but recent studies (Johnson et al., 1964) have shown that they can be used as a hapten to immunize animals against the poison.

## General Consideration of the Algal Toxin Problem

The study of toxins produced by algae has presented many important and fascinating problems, particularly because so many species of algae are potential food supplies for domestic animals and even for humans (Schwimmer and Schwimmer, 1955). Toxic marine algae have caused illness and death in humans through the food chain in fish and shellfish, as illustrated by the occurrence of the shellfish poisons. These occurrences are usually unpredictable, which makes the problem difficult. Ciguatera toxin (Banner et al., 1960; Hessel et al., 1960), which occurs at times in many tropical fish, may be caused by the fish consuming toxic algae. Natives of the South Pacific Islands have died from eating at one time fish that cause no trouble at other times. Many algae

are easy to grow, but some of the toxic ones such as the dinoflagellates are hard to cultivate in axenic culture.  When we can
obtain the various algal toxins in pure form from axenic cultures,
we can properly assess the function of these substances, their
importance to man and animals, and methods for protection against
them.  One of the important problems involving toxic algae at the
present time is the massive fish kills caused by excessive blooms
of G. brevi along the Gulf Coast of Florida.  This problem is worldwide and involves other algae that produce toxins.  As the population
of the world increases and becomes more dependent upon food
sources from the sea, problems with toxic algae will become more
acute.

## References

Abbott, B. C., and D. Ballantine, 1957, J. Mar. Biol. Assoc.
    U.K., 36, 169.

Ballantine, D., and B. C. Abbott, 1957, J. Gen. Microbiol., 16,
    274.

Banner, A. H., P. J. Scheuer, S. Sasaki, P. Helfrich, and C.
    B. Alender, 1960, Ann. N.Y. Acad. Sci., 90, 770.

Bishop, C. T., E. F. L. J. Amet, and P. R. Gorham, 1959,
    Can. J. Biochem. Physiol., 37, 453.

Burke, J. M., J. Marchisotto, J. J. A. McLaughlin, and L.
    Provasoli, 1960, Ann. N.Y. Acad. Sci., 90, 837.

Connell, C. H., and J. B. Cross, 1950, Science, 112, 359.

Dettbarn, W., H. B. Higman, E. Bartels, and T. Podleski, 1965,
    Biochim. Biophys. Acta, 94, 472.

Evans, N. H., 1964, Brit. J. Pharmacol., 22, 478.

Gates, J. A., and W. B. Wilson, 1960, Limnol Oceanog., 5, 171.

Gorham, P. R., 1960, Can. Vet. J., 1, 235.

Grant, G. A., and E. O. Hughes, 1953, Can. J. Public Health,
    44, 334.

Heise, H. A., 1949, J. Allergy, 20, 383.

Heise, H. A., 1951, Ann. Allergy, 9, 100.

Hessel, D. W., B. W. Halstead, and N. H. Peckham, 1960,
    Ann. N.Y. Acad. Sci., 90, 788.

Huges, E. D., P. R. Gorham, and A. Zehnder, 1958, Can. J.
    Microbiol., 4, 225.

Johnson, H. M., P. A. Frey, R. Angelotti, J. E. Campbell, and
    K. H. Lewis, 1964, Proc. Soc. Exptl. Biol. Med., 117, 425.

Kao, C. Y., and A. Fuhrman, 1963, J. Pharm. Exptl. Thera-
peutics, 140, 31.

Kao, C. Y., and A. Nishiyama, 1965a, J. Physiol. (London),
180, 50.

Kao, C. Y., and A. Nishiyama, 1965b, Fed. Proc., 24, 649.

Koch, H. J., 1939, Assoc. Franc. Avan. Sci., Paris, 63rd
Session, 654.

Meyer, K. F., 1953, New England J. Med., 249, 848.

Mold, J. D., J. P. Bowden, D. W. Stanger, J. E. Maurer,
J. M. Lynch, R. S. Wyler, E. J. Schantz, and B. Riegel,
1957, J. Amer. Chem. Soc., 79, 5235.

Nakamura, Y., S. Nakajima, and H. Grundfest, 1965, J. Gen.
Physiol., 48, 985.

Needler, A. B., 1949, J. Fisheries Res. Board Can., 7, 490.

Otterstrom, C. V., and E. Steeman-Nielsen, 1939, Rept. Danish.
Biol. Stat., 44, 5.

Parnas, I., 1963, Israel. J. Zool., 12, 15.

Parnas, I., and B. C. Abbott, 1965, Toxicon, 3, 133.

Parnas, I., K. Reich, and F. Bergmann, 1962, Appl. Microbiol.,
10, 237.

Prakash, A., 1963, J. Fisheries Res. Board Can., 20, 983.

Rahat, M., and T. L. Jahn, 1965, J. Protozool., 12, 246.

Rahat, M., and K. Reich, 1963, J. Gen. Microbiol., 31, 195,
203.

Rapoport, H., M. S. Brown, R. Oesterlin, and W. Schuett, 1964,
147th National Meeting, American Chemical Soc., Phila., Pa.

Ray, S. M., and W. B. Wilson, 1957, Fish Bull. U.S., 123, 57,
469.

Reich, K., and M. Aschner, 1947, J. Botany Jerusalem Ser., 4,
14.

Reich, K., F. Bergmann, and M. Kidron, 1965, Toxicon, 3, 33.

Reich, K., and M. Spiegelstein, 1964, Israel J. Zool., 13, 141.

Riegel, B., D. W. Stanger, D. M. Wikholm, J. D. Mold, and
H. Sommer, 1949, J. Biol. Chem., 177, 7.

Schantz, E. J., J. M. Lynch, G. Vayvada, K. Matsumoto, and
H. Rapoport, 1966, Biochemistry, 5, 1191.

Schantz, E. J., E. F. McFarren, N. L. Schafer, and K. H. Lewis, 1958, J. Assoc. Offic. Agric. Chem., 41, 160.

Schantz, E. J., and H. W. Magnusson, 1964, J. Protozool., 11, 239.

Schantz, E. J., J. D. Mold, D. W. Stanger, J. Shavel, F. J. Riel, J. P. Bowden, J. M. Lynch, R. S. Wyler, B. Riegel, and H. Sommer, 1957, J. Amer. Chem. Soc., 79, 5230.

Schradie, J., and C. A. Bliss, 1962, Lloydia, 25, 214.

Schwimmer, M., and D. Schwimmer, 1955, The Role of Algae and Plankton in Medicine, Grune and Stratton, New York & London.

Shilo, M., and R. F. Rosenberger, 1960, Ann. N.Y. Acad. Sci., 90, 866.

Sommer, H., and K. F. Meyer, 1937, A.M.A. Arch. Pathol., 24, 560.

Sommer, H., W. F. Whedon, C. A. Kofoid, and R. Stohler, 1937, A.M.A. Arch. Pathol., 24, 537.

Tisdale, E. S., 1931, Amer. J. Public Health, 21, 198.

Ulitzer, S., and M. Shilo, 1966, J. Protozool., 13, 332.

Woloszynska, J., and W. Conrad, 1939, Bull. Mus. Hist. Nat. Belg., 15(46), 1.

Yariv, J., and S. Hestrin, 1961, J. Gen. Microbiol., 24, 165.

PART II

FUNGAL TOXINS

# THE CHEMISTRY AND BIOCHEMISTRY OF SPORIDESMINS AND OTHER 2,5-EPIDITHIA-3,6-DIOXOPIPERAZINES

A. Taylor
Atlantic Regional Laboratory
National Research Council
Halifax, Nova Scotia

The chemical evidence for the structures {II: R = H, R' = OH} for sporidesmin and {XVI: R = R' = H} for gliotoxin is critically reviewed. The literature has been examined for other natural products of unknown structure that might be derivatives of 2,5-epidithia-3,6-dioxopiperazine, and a few possibilities, chetomin, in particular, are mentioned. The production of these mold metabolites and the scanty knowledge of their biosynthesis are presented. The toxic effects of these substances on subcellular particles, viruses, bacteria, fungi, plant and animal cells in culture, and plants and animals are summarized and, where applicable, the agricultural significance is mentioned.

At the beginning of this century, Gilruth (1908) described a disease of ruminants in New Zealand that characteristically was not caused by a parasite and for which the symptoms were loss of condition and photosensitization (Clare, 1952; Clare, 1955). In the following sixty years, work on this disease, known as facial eczema (Cunningham et al., 1942; Done et al., 1960; Filmer, 1951; Gilruth, 1908; Hore, 1960; Janes, 1959; McFarlane et al., 1959) although it was not an eczema and had nothing to do with the face, culminated in the discovery that a fungal metabolite, sporidesmin (see Figure 1), characterized as {II: R = H, R' = OH} (Fridrichsons and Mathieson, 1965; Hodges et al., 1963a), was implicated in the disease. This result linked the work in New Zealand with a great deal of work done throughout the world, but particularly in the United States, on the common fungal metabolite gliotoxin, isolated in 1932 by Weindling (Weindling, 1932, 1934, 1937; Weindling and Emerson, 1936). The structure {XVI: R = R' = H} for gliotoxin was proposed in 1958 by Johnson and his collaborators (Bell et al., 1958). This formula differed in many respects from those put forward earlier (see e.g., Johnson, 1955), and the experimental details supporting these revisions have not yet been published. A discussion of the chemistry of gliotoxin is

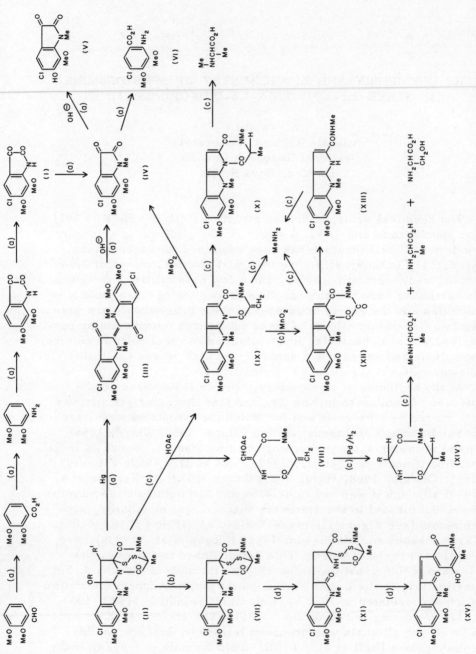

Fig. 1. The sporidesmins and reaction products. (a) Hodges et al., 1963b; (b) Herrmann, Hodges, and Taylor, 1964; (c) Hodges et al., 1964; (d) Hodges, Shannon, and Taylor, 1966b.

therefore deferred until the chemistry of sporidesmin has been
reviewed because a considerable body of experimental evidence
concerning the latter can be best interpreted in terms of an epidithiadioxopiperazine structure.

## Chemistry

Sporidesmins. The sporidesmin metabolites are produced by
Pithomyces chartarum and have been prepared from cultures of
this fungus by a long and tedious isolation procedure (Done et al.,
1961; Ronaldson et al., 1963; Synge and White, 1959; Synge and
White, 1960). The principal biologically active metabolite is
sporidesmin. The molecular formula $C_{18}H_{20}ClN_3O_6S_2$ has been
established despite a distressing tendency to crystallize with approximately one molecule of solvent of crystallization, by analysis (Ronaldson et al., 1963), X-ray crystallography (Fridrichsons
and Mathieson, 1962; Fridrichsons and Mathieson, 1963; Fridrichsons and Mathieson, 1965), and mass spectroscopy (Shannon,
1963). Two O-Me and two N-Me groups were found by analysis,
and the signals at $\tau$ 6.13, 6.18, 6.70, 6.95 ppm were consistent
with this result. The nuclear magnetic resonance spectrum (n.m.r.)
also showed the presence of an aromatic proton and a C-Me group
($\tau$ 7.97 ppm). Sporidesmin gave a diacetate, {II: R = COMe, R' =
OCOMe} (Ronaldson et al., 1963), that had neither acidic nor basic
properties and had no exchangeable protons. When sporidesmin
was treated with mercury, a blue degradation product {$C_{22}H_{20}Cl_2N_2O_6$:
III} and mercuric sulfide were obtained. The blue product was unstable in hot alkaline solution and absorbed at 304, 360, and 647 m$\mu$,
$\tau$ 6.03 and 6.30 ppm and gave strong molecular ion peaks at 582
and 578. By alkaline degradation, two isatins, IV and V, were
isolated and this evidence supported the formulation of the blue
degradation product as the indigo III. This reaction is another
example of the varied rearrangements of 3-hydroxyindolines, the
mechanism of which is unknown. One of the N-methylisatins was
converted to the other, V, on further treatment with alkali, and
the spectroscopic properties of this phenolic isatin V left no doubt
that the hydroxyl group was located at either the 4 or 6 position
(Hodges et al., 1963b). Because the indoxylic carbonyl group
absorbed at 1738 cm$^{-1}$ in both the phenol V and the methoxy compound IV, the carbonyl group was not hydrogen bonded to the phenol,
which was therefore located at the 6 position. The isatin IV together with one mole of ammonia and one of methylamine was obtained when sporidesmin was treated with alkali. In contrast with
this sensitivity to basic conditions, sporidesmin was not readily
degraded in acidic solution. The unsolvated molecule separated
from concentrated hydrochloric acid. However, when heated with
acetic acid, the diacetate was smoothly degraded (Hodges et al.,
1964) and provided a yellow degradation product {$C_{18}H_{16}ClN_3O_4$: IX}

in good yield.   After oxidation with freshly prepared manganese
dioxide, this compound gave the isatin IV.   On vigorous alkaline
hydrolysis, one mole of methylamine was obtained; under milder
conditions, a product $\{C_{15}H_{16}ClN_3O_3: XIII\}$ was isolated.   The same
compound XIII, was also produced from the yellow $C_{18}$ indole IX
in two steps: oxidation of IX with aged manganese dioxide gave the
$C_{17}$ trioxopiperazine XII, and, on alkaline hydrolysis, the $C_{15}$
methylamide XIII was obtained from the latter.   The $C_{18}$ yellow
indole IX, unlike the other degradation products, readily reacted
catalytically with one mole of hydrogen, and the product X, on
hydrolysis, gave not methylamine but N-methylalanine.   The compounds IX, X, XII, and XIII are typical degradation products of an
epidithiadioxopiperazine system.   All have highly characteristic
ultraviolet and mass spectra.   The ultraviolet spectra are shown
in Figure 2, where curve A is typical of compounds IX and XII
and curve B of X and XIII.   An analogous series of compounds
have been obtained as degradation products of dehydrogliotoxin
(Lowe et al., 1966), and Johnson obtained several such compounds

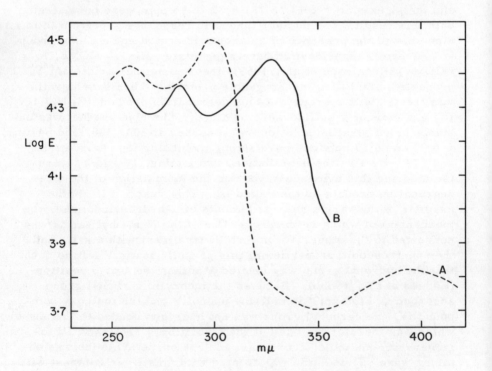

Fig. 2.   Ultraviolet absorption spectra of typical degrada-
tion products of epidithiadioxopiperazines (Curve
A, compounds IX and XII;  Curve B, compounds
X and XIII).

during the course of his work (Dutcher et al., 1944a; Dutcher
et al., 1944b). The mass spectra of compounds like IX, X, XII,
and XIII are also readily recognized (Hodges et al., 1964) because the parent ion is the most intense in the spectrum, and a
high-probability fragmentation involving the expulsion of a moiety
of m/e 83 has now been observed in all of the 12 cases examined
(Ali et al., 1966).

All of these experimental results can be interpreted in terms
of the partial structure -N·CO·C(=CH$_2$)·N-(Me)·CO- for the C$_{18}$
yellow indole IX (Hodges et al., 1964). The acetic acid degradation of sporidesmin diacetate {II: R = COMe, R' = OCOMe} also
gave, in very low yield, a product {VIII: C$_9$H$_{10}$N$_2$O$_4$} (Hodges et
al., 1964), from which a low yield of methylamine was obtained
on acid hydrolysis. However, it absorbed about 3 moles of hydrogen on catalytic reduction, and acid hydrolysis of the product
gave N-methylalanine, alanine, and serine. These facts, together
with the usual spectroscopic properties, establish the structure
of the C$_9$ degradation product as VIII. It will be seen that the
product also contains the partial structure =N·CO·C(=CH$_2$)·
N(Me)·CO- like the C$_{18}$ yellow indole IX. The number of carbon
and nitrogen atoms present in the C$_9$ body VIII, apart from the
acetyl group, was equal to those removed from sporidesmin during
its degradation to the isatin IV. This fact prompts speculation that
the compound was derived from the nonisatinic part of the sporidesmin molecule. The findings were partly supported by our ability to obtain methylamine from sporidesmin and several of its C$_{18}$
degradation products and from VIII but not from the isatin IV. At
this point of our studies, Dr. Mathieson, who was working on the
X-ray crystallography of the sporidesmin methylene dibromide
complex, had arrived at an expression for sporidesmin (Fridrichsons and Mathieson, 1962) that, although it was later modified
(Fridrichsons and Mathieson, 1965), enabled us to fit the isatin IV
and the acid degradation product VIII together. The orientation of
the substituents of the aromatic ring was confirmed by independent
syntheses of the isatin IV and of its related anthranilic acid VI
(Fig. 1, Hodges and Taylor, 1964). The complete X-ray crystallographic analysis of the sporidesmin methylene dibromide
complex established the relative configurations of the atoms
in the molecule but not their absolute configuration (Fridrichsons and Mathieson, 1965). This work is unsatisfactory in some
minor respects owing to our inability to obtain chemical analyses (Ronaldson et al., 1963) that conform to the X-ray analysis
and because the work appears to be unrepeatable in the sense that
the same polymorphic form of the crystals cannot be made (Fridrichsons and Mathieson, 1965). Further chemical evidence for
the expression {II: R = H, R' = OH} was obtained from studies on
sporidesmin-B, a metabolite produced by the mold along with
sporidesmin in about 10% of the yield and easily shown to lack the

secondary hydroxyl group, i.e., {II: R = R' = H}. Like other
3-hydroxyindolines (Finch et al., 1963), the acetoxy derivative
{II: R = COMe, R' = H} was more easily eliminated than the hydroxy group, and the product, anhydrosporidesmin-B VII, was
smoothly rearranged under acid conditions to the expected oxindole XI (Hodges et al., 1966b). These reactions not only establish the nature of the hydroxyl group in sporidesmin-B, they also
provide powerful evidence for the proposed mechanism of this re-
arrangement of 3-hydroxy-3H-indoles (Finch et al., 1963). In
addition, the isolation of anhydrosporidesmin-B gave us the opportunity to show that the absolute configuration of the disulfide
bridge in the sporidesmins and gliotoxins was the same. The
further degradation of the oxindole XI admirably illustrates the
sensitivity of the disulfide bridge to nucleophilic attack. Brief
treatment of a benzene solution with triethylamine gave the oxindole compound XV with bizarre and beautiful properties. For example, seven of its protons were exchanged in the source of the
mass spectrometer (Hodges et al., 1966b), and one of its principal fragmentations in that instrument resulted in the fission of
the indole-methine carbon bond and the transfer of a nonexchange-
able proton. The compound has a very complex n.m.r. spectrum,
possibly due to the numerous tautomers present in solution. There
are three locations (on each carbonyl group) for the charge in its
anion, which then exhibits a large (100 mµ) shift to the visible when
its absorption spectrum is compared with that of the uncharged
molecule.

    In these compounds, the sensitivity of the disulfide group to nu-
cleophilic attack forms the basis of their estimation. Thus adequate
estimation of sporidesmin in fermentation liquors was possible by
an adaptation of the iodometric penicillin assay (Clare, 1963; Done
et al., 1961). However, a much greater sensitivity was achieved
by using the ability of the disulfides to catalyze the reaction

$$2N_3^- + I_2 = 3N_2 + 2I^-$$

(Clare, 1963; Clare and Gumbley, 1962; Clare and Mortimer,
1964; Marbrook, 1964; Russell, 1960; Russell, 1962). The disulfides are more efficient catalysts of this reaction (Dahl and
Pardue, 1965) than other sulfur-containing substances, e.g.,
cystine; about 1.75 ml of nitrogen are released per µmole of gliotoxin present. They can be estimated either by titration of the
iodine consumed or by manometric estimation of the nitrogen
evolved. The latter procedure is especially valuable because it
can often be carried out in the presence of biological material
(Brewer and Taylor, 1966). A further use of the lability of the
disulfides, and one which in my experience is very characteristic,
is their ability to form silver sulfide when treated with neutral,
aqueous silver nitrate. This reaction allows their detection on
thin-layer plates in quantities of less than 0.1 µg.

Gliotoxins.  All of these analytical properties are exhibited by
gliotoxin (Johnson et al., 1943).  Johnson, Woodward, and collaborators used Trichoderma viride for the production of gliotoxin
for chemical studies.  When we became interested in gliotoxin, we
used Penicillium terlikowskii (HLX 136*) to produce it (see Table 2,
p. 83), but the product obtained had different physical properties
from a specimen of gliotoxin kindly provided by Professor R. B.
Woodward (Taylor, 1966).  When the P. terlikowskii metabolite
was boiled with methanol, material with physical properties identical to the authentic sample was obtained.  Recently, I have
checked the physical properties of the metabolite produced by T.
viride and have found them to be identical with those of the compound from P. terlikowskii.  Thus the material used by Johnson
was probably an isomer.  Preliminary n.m.r. spectroscopy in this
laboratory suggests that the two compounds are epimeric at the
carbon atom in XVI bearing the secondary hydroxyl group.  (See
Figure 3.)  The stable isomer used by Johnson was shown to have
the molecular formula $C_{13}H_{14}N_2O_4S_2$.  It reacted with aromatic acid
chlorides to give crystalline derivatives that were diesters on the
basis of their analysis (Bruce et al., 1944).  In no case, however,
was gliotoxin regenerated by hydrolysis.  Johnson noted (1955),
and we have confirmed, that these compounds are biologically inactive.  Upon reduction with aluminum amalgam, gliotoxin gives
a number of degradation products including hydrogen sulfide.  From
this mixture, Johnson and his co-workers (Dutcher et al., 1945;
Johnson and Buchanan, 1953) were able to isolate a product
$C_{13}H_{16}N_2O_4$ {XVII: R = R = H} that was shown by Elvidge and Spring
(1949b) to give a crystalline diacetate.  Similar reaction conditions used later (Bell, 1956) on dehydrodesthiogliotoxin XXII resulted in dehydration.  Desthiogliotoxin XVII was further degraded
by two routes.  In the first it was shown that dehydration occurred
(Elvidge and Spring, 1949a; Johnson and Buchanan, 1953) in the
presence of acid to give anhydrodesthiogliotoxin that was different
from {XVIII: R = OH, R' = H} (Harper, 1954; Johnson and Andreen,
1950).  Further treatment of this compound with alkali and closure
of the dioxopiperazine ring gave 1, 2, 3, 4-tetrahydro-2, 3-dimethyl-
1,4-dioxopyrazino[1, 2-a]indole {XIX} as shown by an unambiguous
synthesis XXXI → XXXII → XXXIII (Dutcher et al., 1944a; Johnson
et al., 1945; Johnson et al., 1947).  This pyrazinoindole contains
all the carbon and nitrogen atoms found in gliotoxin.  This conclusion was supported by determination of the structures of three
degradation products derived directly from the metabolite.  The
first, 2,3-dimethyl-pyrazino[1,2-a]indole, was obtained by reduction of gliotoxin with phosphorus and hydrogen iodide (Dutcher et
al., 1944a).  Second, the related trioxoderivative XXI was the

*Refers to collection of microorganisms held in this laboratory.

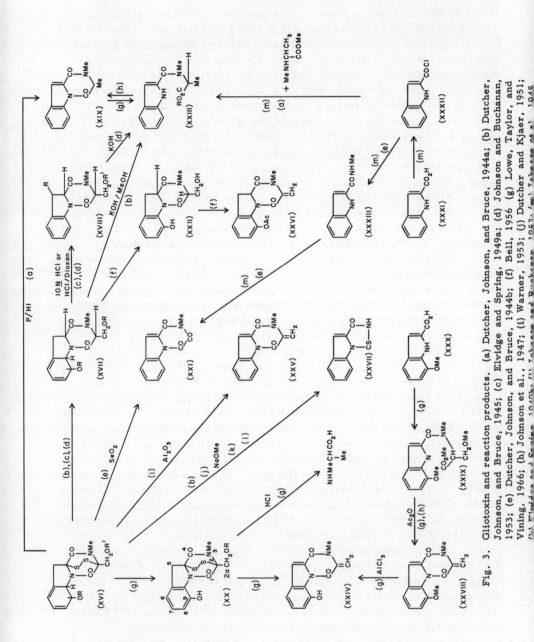

Fig. 3. Gliotoxin and reaction products. (a) Dutcher, Johnson, and Bruce, 1944a; (b) Dutcher, Johnson, and Bruce, 1945; (c) Elvidge and Spring, 1949a; (d) Johnson and Buchanan, 1953; (e) Dutcher, Johnson, and Bruce, 1944b; (f) Bell, 1956 (g) Lowe, Taylor, and Vining, 1966; (h) Dutcher, Johnson et al., 1947; (i) Warner, 1953; (j) Dutcher and Kjaer, 1951; (k) Johnson and Spring, 1949b; (l) Johnson and Buchanan, 1953; (m) Taylor et al., 1945

product of dehydrogenation with selenium (Dutcher et al., 1944b),
and finally the 2-methylene-3-methylpyrazino[1,2-a]indole XXV
was obtained when gliotoxin was treated with alumina (Warner,
1953). All of these were synthesized unambiguously. The second
series of degradation reactions of desthiogliotoxin XVII has been
reported in detail only in student theses (Harper, 1954). When
XVII was treated with palladium in boiling xylene, a phenol was
obtained in 5% yield, for which the expression XXII was given.
Further treatment of XXII with acetic anhydride gave a phenolic
acetate XXVI in which a further olefinic bond had been generated.
It was considered to be an indoline because of its ultraviolet spectrum; both XXII and XXVI absorbed in the 290 to 300 mμ region.
This argument now appears a little tenuous because most 9-
hydroxy-(and methoxy)-pyrazino[1,2-a]indoles absorb at these
frequencies (Lowe et al., 1966). The only available evidence for
the location of the sulfur atoms in the pyrazinoindole system came
from the isolation of the thiohydantoin XXVII (Dutcher et al., 1945;
Dutcher and Kjaer, 1951; Elvidge and Spring, 1949b; Johnson and
Buchanan, 1951), which suggested the sulfur was linked to the
noncarbonyl carbon atoms of the dioxopiperazine ring. All of this
evidence was interpreted in terms of several expressions for gliotoxin, the formula {XVI: R = R' = H} being the latest proposed.
This stands as a remarkable testimony to the power of the induc-
tive method in natural product chemistry and should give skeptics
of its latter-day manifestations, e.g., molecular genetics, a
moment's introspection. It has been confirmed in every detail
by X-ray crystallographic analysis (Beecham et al., 1966). However, perhaps the most significant observation concerning gliotoxin chemistry was that of Braude and Lowe, who showed that
gliotoxin reduced one mole of o-chloranil and was itself oxidized
to a product {$C_{13}H_{12}N_2O_4S_2$: XX}. This compound has been shown
to be present in cultures of Penicillium terlikowskii together with
an isomer that differs only in the orientation of the phenolic hydroxyl group (Lowe et al., 1966). It is biologically active and
forms a biologically active monoacetate {XX, R = COMe}. When
the latter was treated with base under the conditions described
earlier for isosporidesmin-B XI, 1,2,3,4-tetrahydro-9-hydroxy-
2-methylene-3-methyl-1,4-dioxopyrazino[1,2-a]indole XXIV was
obtained in 90% yield. The structure of this degradation product
was proved by synthesis from 7-methoxyindole-2-carboxylic acid
as shown in the scheme (Lowe et al., 1966). The most noteworthy
point of the synthesis is the easy demethylation of the methyl ether
XXVIII and our inability to methylate the phenol XXIV. This synthesis has proved of general application and thus this heterocyclic
system is now readily available. The synthesis established the
orientation of one of the hydroxyl groups in dehydrogliotoxin. The
mode of its formation from the latter, by analogy with the corresponding sporidesmin derivatives, strongly supports the proposed

(Beecham et al., 1966; Bell et al., 1958) position of the disulfide bridge. The nature and location of the remaining oxygen atom were determined by examination of the n.m.r. spectrum of dehydrogliotoxin that showed the presence of two methylene groups (Figure 4); the remaining oxygen atom was part of a hydroxyl

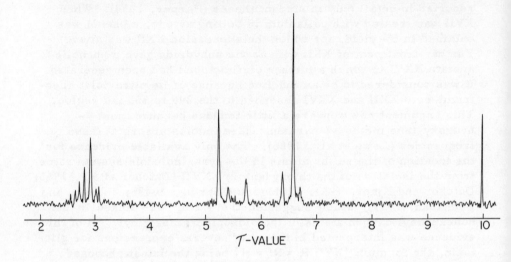

Fig. 4.   Nuclear magnetic resonance spectrum of dehydro-
            gliotoxin.

group located at position 2a. It is clear that the gliotoxin studied by Johnson and his co-workers was a dihydro derivative of XX but, apart from the disulfide group, the geometry of the tetrahydroindole system is uncertain at the moment. The preparation and isolation of dehydrogliotoxin gave a derivative whose only asymmetric centers were those bearing the disulfide bridge, and it was in this way analogous to anhydrosporidesmin-B VII where similar molecular parameters obtain. The optical rotary dispersion curves of the two compounds both showed negative Cotton effects at different frequencies because one was an indole and the other an indoline. Although the optical rotary dispersion (o.r.d.) curves of sporidesmin, sporidesmin-B, and gliotoxin differed greatly, we were delighted to find that their circular dichroism curves were almost superimposable. It was concluded that the absolute configurations at the disulfide bridge in the sporidesmin series and the gliotoxin series was the same. Mathieson and his co-workers have been able to define the absolute configuration of one of the gliotoxins (Beecham et al., 1966) by using the f'' component of the sulfur atoms (Bijvoet et al., 1951; Patterson, 1963; Peterson, 1955). It is uncertain at the moment which of the two isomers was examined because no physical properties of the material (apart from the unit cell dimensions) were given. They used

the circular dichroism data (Herrmann et al., 1964) mentioned
earlier to determine the absolute configuration of the asymmetric
centers in the sporidesmin molecule and concurred in the conclusion that the asymmetry of the disulfide bridge was the same
in sporidesmin and in gliotoxin. They also showed that the corresponding asymmetric bridgehead carbon atoms in the gliotoxin
examined and in sporidesmin had the opposite stereochemistry.
There remains, therefore, the question whether this is a true
difference in stereochemistry or whether one of the compounds
for which an X-ray crystallographic analysis is available is an
artifact. Both possibilities have important biosynthetic conse-
quencies. A further interesting point arising from the X-ray
studies (Beecham and Mathieson, 1966) concerns the rule relat-
ing the sign of the circular dichroism associated with cisoid skew
dienes to the chirality of these chromophores. The rule apparently does not hold in the case of gliotoxin where a positive dichroism is associated with a left-handed skew.

Apart from the stereochemical problems discussed in the preceding paragraph, there are a number of other problems of gliotoxin chemistry that are outstanding. It is not clear how derivatives of alanine are produced when gliotoxin, dehydrogliotoxin,
and desthiogliotoxin are hydrolyzed under acidic conditions; it is
not known which of the hydroxyl groups are esterified in the naturally occurring acetate (Johnson et al., 1953), and the orientation of the hydroxyl group in the naturally occurring isomer of
dehydrogliotoxin is also unknown.

Chetomin. In 1944, Waksman and Bugie reported the production
by an isolate of Chetomium cochliodes of a metabolite with antibacterial properties that could be extracted from the mycelium
(Geiger et al., 1944), and it was called chetomin. Later, Geiger
(1949) attempted to purify this material but was unable to obtain
a crystalline sample. Analysis of his amorphous material suggested the formula $C_{16}H_{17}N_3O_4S_2$. The analytical samples had
$[\alpha]_D^{22}$ 360° (c, 1, CHCl₃) and $\lambda_{max}$ (EtOH) 278, 287, 297 mμ $E_{1\,cm}^{1\%}$
148, 155, 148. Geiger (1949) investigated the effects of a number
of reagents on the biological activity of his material. He showed
that chetomin was inactivated at pH 9 after 24 hours in hot 20%
hydrochloric acid and by a variety of oxidizing agents. On alkaline
hydrolysis, carbon dioxide and ammonia were obtained although
the characterization of the latter was doubtful. Chetomin reacted
with sodium plumbite giving lead sulfide, and, judging by certain
color reactions of the compound and of its poorly characterized
degradation products, Geiger concluded that an indole nucleus
was present. My colleague Dr. Vining suggested to me that
chetomin was possibly another example of an epidithiadioxopiperazine. A number of isolates of Chetomium cochliodes were therefore examined, and contrary to Waksman's statement (Waksman
and Bugie, 1944), although this might have been expected from the

work of Tveit (Tveit and Moore, 1954), it was found that almost
all the specimens examined produced antibacterial metabolites
(see Table 2, p. 83). Extracts of culture filtrates have the property of catalyzing the decomposition of azide with iodine, but, in
agreement with Waksman (Geiger et al., 1944), we have found
that the greatest quantities of these metabolites are found in the
mycelium. Chromatography of such extracts on silicic acid-coated
plates showed the presence of several metabolites that react with
silver nitrate in the manner described here. Through the gener-
osity of Dr. Waksman we have obtained his original isolate and
have found that its production of antibacterial metabolites in culture is erratic. Predominantly one metabolite was found in some
cultures, and we were fortunate in finding an isolate from Nappan,
Nova Scotia, that produces this material in considerably greater
yield. Partition chromatography of the apparently single substance showed that it was a mixture. It has been possible to obtain from this mixture material that has a Gaussian distribution
on partition chromatography in the systems carbon disulfide:
methanol:water 5:5:0.2 and benzene:chloroform:methanol:water
15:15:23:7. Its physical properties are close to those described
by Geiger, i.e., $[\alpha]_D^{22}$ 340 (c, 1, $CHCl_3$) $\lambda_{max}$ (MeOH) 276, 284,
293 m$\mu$ $E_{1 cm}^{1\%}$ 170, 185, 172), and the best analytical evidence
at the moment suggests the empirical formula $C_{16}H_{18}N_2O_5S_2$, although this is only regarded as tentative. Two N-Me groups have
been found analytically and confirmed by the signals at $\tau$ 6.80,
6.82 ppm (Figure 5). About two moles of methylamine are pro-

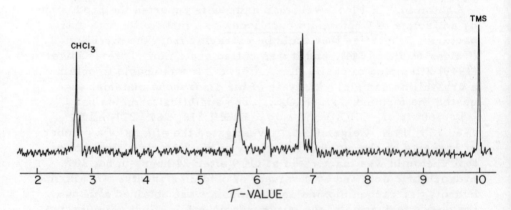

Fig. 5. Nuclear magnetic resonance spectrum of chetomin.

duced on acid hydrolysis. The similar location of the two N-
methylamide groups is also indicated by the strong absorption
at 1685 cm$^{-1}$, which we have been unable to resolve. As with
dehydrogliotoxin, N-methylalanine is found in hydrolysates. All
of this evidence, together with the biological results that follow,
suggest that chetomin has the partial structure XXXIV (Figure 6).

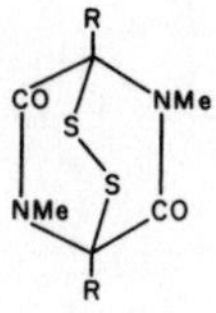

Fig. 6.  Partial structure of chetomin.

Other Disulfides.  The possibility that other disulfides of this
type have been isolated but remain unrecognized is worth con-
sideration.  If the candidates among natural products be restricted
to those having growth-inhibitory properties, there are at least
500 antibiotics of unknown structure reported in the literature.
Many can be eliminated on the basis of their physical and chemical properties, but often insufficient data are given for a decision
on this basis.  Table 1 lists compounds that are known to contain
C, H, N, O, and S; lose their biological activity in alkaline solution; and absorb at frequencies typical of epidithiadioxopiperazines.  A number of compounds, such as echinomycins (Corbaz
et al., 1957), bottromycins (Waisvisz et al., 1957), and X 1008
(Berger et al., 1957), which yield thiazole derivatives on vigorous
acid hydrolysis, should perhaps have been included along with
quinomycins and micrococcins.  It seems reasonable (Herrmann
et al., 1964; Lowe et al., 1966) to envisage the conversion of this
type of disulfide to a thiazole under such conditions, although this
has not yet been demonstrated.

## Biochemistry

Producing Organisms.  Organisms known to produce epidithiadioxopiperazines on laboratory cultivation are given in Table 2.
All of these organisms are found commonly in soils; Pithomyces
chartarum* is usually found in tropical and subtropical latitudes
(but see Gregory and Lacey, 1964; Lacey and Gregory, 1962).
The question of production of these disulfides by the organisms
when growing in soil has been the source of considerable debate
(see, e.g., Brian, 1946b; Tveit, 1955; Tveit, 1956; Tveit and
Moore, 1954; Weindling, 1938; Weindling and Faucett, 1936).
This topic has been studied intensively in New Zealand in recent
years because of the implication that Pithomyces chartarum is
part of the etiology of facial eczema (Brook, 1959; Brook, 1963;
Brook, 1964; Crawley et al., 1961; Hore, 1960; Janes, 1959;
Percival, 1959; Percival and Thornton, 1958; Sinclair, 1961;
Smith and Crawley, 1962; Smith and Crawley, 1964; Smith et al.,

---

*This name is now accepted instead of the synonym Sporides-
mium bakeri Syd. on the basis of Ellis's work (M. B. Ellis, Mycol.
Papers No. 76).

# Table 1. Some Antibiotics of Unknown Structure Possibly Derivatives of Epidithiadioxopiperazine

| Antibiotic | Organism | Biological | Spectroscopic Properties | Elementary Composition | Refs. |
|---|---|---|---|---|---|
| Antibiotic fraction C | Epidermophyton floccosum | Antibacterial | $\lambda_{max}$ 6.87, 6.32 μ | | (1) |
| Antibiotic 9671 R.P. | Streptomyces 40, 037 S. actinosus | Antibacterial | $\lambda_{max}$ 242, 322 mμ | C, 49.6; H, 4.0; N, 14.4; O, 16.7; S, 15.8% | (2) |
| Antibiotic 9971 R.P. | Streptomyces gascariensis | Antitumor Antifungal | | | (3) |
| Althiomycin | Streptomyces althioricus | Antibacterial | $\lambda_{max}$ (HCl) 285 mμ $\lambda_{max}$ (NaOH) 300 mμ $\nu_{max}$ 1710, 1685, 1654 cm$^{-1}$ | $C_{15}H_{14}N_4O_6S_2$ $C_{27}H_{28}N_8O_{10}S_3$ | (4) |
| M5-8450 | Penicillium sp. | Antiviral | | | (5) |
| Matamycin | Streptomyces matensis | Antibacterial | $\lambda_{max}$ 5.95, 6.15 μ $\lambda_{max}$ (MeOH) 290 mμ $\left(E_{1\ cm}^{1\%}\ 200\right)$ $\lambda_{max}$ (0.1 N NaOH) 310 mμ $\left(E_{1\ cm}^{1\%}\ 275\right)$ | C, 43.95; H, 4.06 N, 14.45; S, 13.57% | (6) |
| Micrococcins (Pumilin) | Bacillus pumilis | Antibacterial | $\lambda_{max}$ 345 mμ $\nu_{max}$ 1655 cm$^{-1}$ | $(C_8H_9N_2O_2S)_m$ | (7) |
| Phalamycin | Streptomyces noursei | Antibacterial | $\lambda_{max}$ 345 mμ, $\nu_{max}$ 1655 cm$^{-1}$ | C, 50.1; H, 4.78 N, 14.98; S, 3.67% | (8) |
| Quinomycin | Streptomyces sp. | Antibacterial Toxic to He La cells in culture | $\lambda_{max}$ 320 mμ $\nu_{max}$ 1743, 1692, 1650 cm$^{-1}$ | C, 54.67; H, 6.39 N, 13.64; S, 5.54% | (9) |
| Raromycin | Streptomyces albochromogenes | Antibacterial Antitumor | $\lambda_{max}$ 268 mμ, $\nu_{max}$ 1670 cm$^{-1}$ | C, 57.53; H, 8.03; N, 4.46; S, ? % | (10) |
| Sparsomycin | Streptomyces sparsogenes var. sparsogenes | Antibacterial Antitumor | $\lambda_{max}$ 270, 302 mμ, $\nu_{max}$ 1730, 1660 cm$^{-1}$ | $C_{13}H_{21}N_3O_6S_2$ | (11) |
| Taitomycin | Streptomyces afghaniensis | Antibacterial | $\lambda_{max}$ 330, 420 mμ | C, 53.57; H, 4.87; N, 9.50; S, ? % | (12) |
| Thioaurin | Streptomyces sp. | Antibacterial | $\lambda_{max}$ 232, 370 mμ, $\lambda_{max}$ 6.01, 6.50 μ | $C_{14}H_{12}N_4O_4S_4$ | (13) |
| Thiomycin | Streptomyces phaeochromogenes (like) | Antibacterial | $\lambda_{max}$ (MeOH) 370 mμ $\lambda_{max}$ (0.5 N NaOH) 300 mμ $\lambda_{max}$ 5.95, 6.05 μ | C, 49.6; H, 5.50 N, 8.88; S, 16.26% | (14) |
| Unamycin | Streptomyces fungicidus | Antifungal | $\lambda_{max}$ 236, 273, $\nu_{max}$ 1670 cm$^{-1}$ | C, 46.4; H, 4.4; N, 22.7; S, 2.27% | (15) |

(1) Katagiri and Sato, 1961. (2) Rhone-Poulenc, 1963. (3) Rhone-Poulenc, 1965. (4) Cram et al., 1963; Yamaguchi et al., 1957. (5) Hull and Lavelle, 1953; Powell et al., 1952. (6) Margalith et al., 1959; Sen et al., 1959. (7) Brookes et al., 1960b; Brookes et al., 1957; Dean et al., 1961; Fuller, 1955; Heatley and Doery, 1951; Heatley et al., 1952; Kelly et al., 1952; Mijovic and Walker, 1960; Mijovic and Walker 1961; Su, 1948. (8) Brown, 1956; Brown and Hazen, 1953. (9) Katagiri and Sugiura, 1961; Shionogi, 196 Yoshida, 1962. (10) Sumiki and Umezawa, 1960. (11) Argoudelis and Herr, 1962; Owen et al., 1962; Pit tillo et al., 1965; Slechta, 1965; Upjohn Co., 1965. (12) Komatsu et al., 1959; Ogawa et al., 1963; Shim et al., 1959; Shimo and Tomosugi, 1960; Tomosugi et al., 1959. (13) Bolhofer et al., 1953. (14) Hinum et al., 1955. (15) Nagase et al., 1959.

Note:
  Since this table was compiled it has become clear that antibiotic 9971 R P and sparsomycin ar not epidi thiadioxopiperazines. The author wishes to thank colleagues of the Upjohn Co. for a gift of sparsomycin.

Table 2.   Microorganisms Known to Produce Epidithiadioxopiperazines in Culture

| Organism | Place of Isolation (when known) | Antibiotic Produced | Yield (μg/ml) | Refs. |
|---|---|---|---|---|
| Chaetomium cochliodes HLX 577 | Pea seed, Ontario, 1945 | Chetomin | 3.6 | (1) |
| C. cochliodes ATCC 10195 HLX 374 | | Chetomin | 7-15 | (2) |
| C. cochliodes HLX 240 | Soil, Nappan, Nova Scotia | Chetomin | >20 | (3) |
| Gliocladium fimbriatum (Trichoderma viride) | | Gliotoxin | 50-80 | (4) |
| Aspergillus fumigatus | | Gliotoxin + 1 Unknown | 20-80 | (5) |
| Aspergillus sp. | | Gliotoxin | | (6) |
| Penicillium obscurum (Biourge) ? terlikowskii | | Gliotoxin | | (7) |
| P. cinerascens | Soil, Cumberland United Kingdom | Gliotoxin | | (8) |
| P. terlikowskii NRRL A573 HLX 441 | | Isodehydrogliotoxin Gliotoxin Acetate Gliotoxin + 2 Unknown | 272 | (9) |
| P. terlikowskii HLX 136 | | Dehydrogliotoxin Gliotoxin | 180 | (10) |
| Penicillium sp. | Bath, Maine, U.S.A. Anvers, Belgium | | | (11) |
| Pithomyces chartarum (Bert & Curt) M. B. Ellis C.M.I. 74473 HLX | High-sporing sector from plate exposed at Hamilton, New Zealand | Sporidesmin Sporidesmin-B | 0.3 | (12) |
| P. chartarum S 73a HLX 673 (and other wild isolates) | Debris of Paspalum dilatatum, Mount Albert, Auckland, New Zealand | Sporidesmin | 1.5 | (13) |

D. Brewer, A. Taylor (unpublished data). (2) Geiger et al., 1944; Tveit, 1956; Waksman and Bugie, 44. (3) D. Brewer, A. Taylor (unpublished data). (4) Brian, 1944; Brian and Hemming, 1945; Elvidge d Spring, 1949a; Elvidge and Spring, 1949b; Haenseler and Allen, 1934; Johnson et al., 1943; Weindling, 32; Weindling, 1934; Weindling, 1937; Weindling and Emerson, 1936; Tveit, 1955. (5) Betina and Ba- h, 1964; Glister and Williams, 1944; Menzel et al., 1944; Waksman et al., 1943. (6) Stanley, 1944; nley and Mills, 1946. (7) Mull et al., 1945. (8) Bracken and Raistrick, 1947. (9) Johnson et al., 1953; Taylor (unpublished data). (10) Brian, 1946a; Brian, 1946b; Lowe et al., 1966. (11) Betina et al., 1; Johnson et al., 1944; Nemec et al., 1960; Rightsel et al., 1964. (12) Dingley, 1962; Dingley et al., 2; Done et al., 1961; Lloyd and Clarke, 1959; Percival, 1959; Percival and Thornton, 1958; Ross, 0a; Ross, 1960b; Ross, 1962; Ross and Thornton, 1962; Thornton and Percival, 1959. (13) Dingley, 2; Dingley et al., 1962; Gregory and Lacey, 1964; Lacey and Gregory, 1962; Ross, 1960a; Ross, 0b; Ross, 1962.

1961a; Smith et al., 1961b; Smith et al., 1962a; Smith et al.,
1962b; Smith et al., 1963; Thornton and Percival, 1959; Thornton and Ross, 1959; Thornton and Sinclair, 1960). This assumption has received support from experiments designed to control
the disease by control of the spread of the fungus on pastureland
(Brook and Mutch, 1964; Mutch and Brook, 1964; Thornton, 1963a;
Thornton, 1963b; Thornton and Taylor, 1963); by the demonstration of typical, albeit nontoxic, fungal metabolites in extracts of
toxic pasture (Perrin, 1959; Russell et al., 1962; Sandos et al.,
1959; White, 1958b); and by the isolation of toxic material from
pasture by White (1958a; Perrin et al., 1953; Russell, 1962;
Simpson et al., 1957), one of the most notable of recent achieve-
ments in natural product chemistry. The disease also occurs in
areas where the climate is conducive to the growth of fungi (Mitchell et al., 1961; Mitchell et al., 1959; Packard, 1960). However, it should be noted that the mere presence of a fungus does
not of necessity mean that these metabolites are also present. In
the case of P. chartarum, several isolates from pasture produced
only 5 µg/1 when grown in the laboratory (Dingley et al., 1962;
Ross, 1962), and this may be the reason why surveys of pasture
fungi (Cunningham, 1958; Neill, 1940), prior to that of Thornton
(Thornton and Ross, 1959), did not reveal organisms able to produce these metabolites. If it is assumed that the organisms included in Table 2 produce these disulfides when growing in soils,
then one important mechanism for the intoxication of grazing animals would be the translocation of the fungal metabolites by the
edible herbage. Evidence for such translocation of "chetomin" in
oat seedlings and other grasses has been obtained by Tveit (1956;
Tveit and Moore, 1954). He also obtained some evidence that during the translocation process chetomin was metabolized by oat
seedlings to give material of greater antifungal activity (Tveit and
Wood, 1955). Matthews (personal communication) has obtained ra-
dioautographic evidence that $^{35}$S-labeled sporidesmin is similarly
translocated by perennial rye grass seedlings. It should, however,
be noted that in both of these cases neither the metabolite presented nor the material in the plant was adequately characterized.

   Biosynthesis. Of the organisms included in Table 2, Penicillium terlikowskii (HLX 441) produces the epidithiadioxopiperazine
ring system in greatest amount on a simple, chemically defined
medium. Another isolate of this fungus, HLX 136, also gives
high yields and has a further advantage that 90% of the disulfides
produced is gliotoxin. In our hands, the high-sporing isolate of
P. terlikowskii (HLX 238) produces only 5 to 10% of the amount
of crude gliotoxin produced by the isolates listed in Table 2, although Brian (1946b) obtained the opposite result. The isolate
HLX 136 in submerged shaken cultures produces 50 to 80 µg/ml/
day of crude gliotoxin between the tenth and thirteenth day of cultivation. It is therefore an admirable organism for studying the

biosynthesis of the epidithiadioxopiperazine ring system. Very
little is known about this process. Aspergillus fumigatus does not
produce gliotoxin when grown on media deficient in sulfur (Menzel
et al., 1944), and evidence has been obtained (Brook and Matthews,
1960; Marbrook and Matthews, 1962) that $^{35}SO_4^{-2}$ is incorporated
into sporidesmin, although in the latter case the metabolite was not
characterized chemically. It is easy to speculate, after examination of formulas II and XVI, that the biosynthesis of sporidesmin
involves the cyclization and reduction of a tryptophanylalanine in-
termediate and in a similar way that gliotoxin biosynthesis occurs
by an analogous reductive cyclization of a phenylalanylserine.
Suhadolnik and Chenoweth (1958) and Winstead and Suhadolnik (1960)
have obtained some evidence that this speculation is true in the
case of gliotoxin. They found that DL-phenylalanine-1- and -2-$^{14}$C,
DL-phenylalanine-?-T, and DL-m-tyrosine-?-T were incorporated
into the antibiotic by Trichoderma viride to the extent of 4.2 to 8.4%,
6.9 to 12.4%; 14.2 to 17.6%; and 30.8 to 44.3%, respectively. The
methyl radical of the N-Me group was derived from the S-Me group
of methionine or from carbon-3 of serine-3-$^{14}$C. Serine-1- and
-3-$^{14}$C were incorporated into the pyrazine ring, although 19% of
the label in the latter case was found in the indole-2-carboxylic
acid XXXI obtained from the radioactive gliotoxin by degradation
XVI → XVII → XXXI. My colleague M. S. Ali has recently obtained similar results after growing Penicillium terlikowskii (HLX
136) in the presence of ring labeled $^{14}$C-DL-phenylalanine and
$CT_3 \cdot NH_2CH \cdot CO_2H$. The results obtained by Suhadolnik led him to
propose the scheme phe → m-tyr → XVII → XVI for the biosynthesis of gliotoxin. It will be concluded that many of the most interesting questions concerning gliotoxin biosynthesis, e.g., what
is the mechanism of closure of the heterocyclic rings; how are the
peptide bonds formed; when and how is the sulfur incorporated,
remain to be answered. Recently we have isolated the phenol XXIV
from surface cultures of Penicillium terlikowskii (Ali and Taylor,
1966) where dehydrogliotoxin XX is also produced (Lowe et al.,
1966), and it is therefore possible that a reversal of the reaction
XX → XXIV occurs in the fermentation.* Interesting problems in
the biosynthesis of sporidesmin include questions about the timing
and manner in which the substituents are introduced into the trypto-
phanyl moiety. A synthesis of the related anthranilic acid has been
reported (Hodges and Taylor, 1964), but suitable isotopically labeled material has not yet been prepared.

## Toxicology

The effects of epidithiadioxopiperazines on living systems (including virus and subcellular particles) are defined, for the pur-

---

*The addition of sulfur dichloride transannularly across uncon-
jugated cyclic dienes has recently been reported (Corey and Block,
1966; Lautenschlaeger, 1966; Weil et al., 1966).

poses of this review, as their toxicology. Emphasis is placed on
biochemical findings, and pathological aspects of the work are
merely covered by references to the original papers. The section is divided according to the kind of biological system studied.

Subcellular Particles. Sporidesmin at a concentration of 160 μM
did not affect the integrity of the lysosomal membrane (Slater et
al., 1964). This conclusion is in agreement with in vivo studies
on rats dosed with 6 mg/kg (Slater and Greenbaum, 1965; Slater
et al., 1963). The effects of sporidesmin on mitochondrial enzymes using intact liver mitochondria from rats (Gallagher, 1964a;
Rimington et al., 1962; Slater et al., 1964), guinea pigs (Wright
and Forrester, 1965), and sheep (Wright and Forrester, 1965)
have been examined, but the results obtained by the different workers do not always agree. Thus it has been stated (Rimington et al.
1962; Slater et al., 1964) that the effects of sporidesmin on rat
liver are probably not significantly related to mitochondrial swelling and failure of NADH$_2$ oxidation because the metabolite had no
effect on the former at 30 to 80 μM and, in fact, increased oxygen
uptake by mitochondria in the presence of L-malate or α-oxoglutarate as substrate at 2000 μM. By contrast, it has been claimed
(Gallagher, 1964a) that sporidesmin at 3.3 μM inhibits the oxidation of L-malate by rat liver mitochondria and that oxidation is
also inhibited at a concentration of 330 μM α-oxoglutarate. This
difference does not appear to be due to differences in technique
because all were using the same assay procedure. A similar discrepancy concerning the induction of mitochondrial swelling by
sporidesmin may be resolved on the following basis. Gallagher
(1964a) found that 0.02 to 10 μM sporidesmin induced mitochondrial
swelling, a process inhibited by 1000 μM EDTA or ATP. The absence of mitochondrial swelling reported by others (Slater et al.,
1964; Wright and Forrester, 1965) may therefore have been due
to traces of EDTA in the mitochondrial preparations. Gallagher
(1964a) thought that the inhibition of oxidation of L-malate by
sporidesmin was due to leakage of NAD through the permeable
mitochondrial membrane and showed that addition of NAD reversed
the inhibition. However, it is also necessary to add that the effect
of additional NAD was seen only in the presence of added glutathion
and nicotinamide. If the effect of sporidesmin on NAD-linked enzymes systems is dependent on a reduction of the concentration of
cofactors because of their diffusion through the mitochondrial membrane, it is clear that mitochondrial swelling may be a prerequi-
site for observation of the effect. This may explain the apparent
differences in result mentioned above. All workers are agreed
that succinate oxidation is unaffected by sporidesmin at concentrations less than 330 μM and that oxidative phosphorylation is
also unaffected. Thus respiratory inhibition is concerned with the
oxidation of substrates that require nicotinamide coenzymes. Similar results have been obtained using liver mitochondria from shee

and guinea pigs (Wright and Forrester, 1965), where, however,
the difference in results, particularly with respect to mitochondrial swelling, may be the result of species differences. The
general conclusion seems to be that the effect of sporidesmin on
the respiration of liver homogenates and mitochondria is observed only at much higher concentrations than are required to
halt growth of, e.g., epithelial cells (see following paragraph),
i.e., 300 $\mu$M as compared to 0.06 $\mu$M, the latter being the order
of concentration shown by Gallagher to have an effect on mitochondrial swelling (1964a). It is therefore clear that further
work is required on the action of sporidesmin on mitochondrial
membrane function.

Virus. It was shown several years ago (Asheshov et al., 1949;
Hanson and Eble, 1949) that culture filtrates of Aspergillus fumigatus inhibited the growth of several bacteriophages in the
presence of host bacteria, but later (Hall et al., 1951) these
workers noted that gliotoxin did not permit the growth of Staphylococcus, Enterococcus, Escherichia coli, Bacillus subtilis, and
others in the presence of infecting bacteriophages. Although some
isolates of A. fumigatus produce fumagillin, an active inhibitor of
bacteriophage, this point should be reexamined in view of the reported antiviral activity of gliotoxin (Larin et al., 1965; Rightsel
et al., 1964). Rightsel et al. (1964) reported that gliotoxin XVI
and its naturally occurring acetate {XVI: R or R' = COMe, R or
R' = H} inhibited the multiplication of poliovirus, herpes, and
Asian influenza in cultures of monkey kidney, HEp2 and KB cell
cultures in suspension or in monolayers. No activity was observed against vaccinia, measles, Coxsackie B, and other viruses
under the same conditions. They were unable to obtain a therapeutic effect in mice challenged intracerebrally with 10 or 32 $LD_{50}$
type 2 poliovirus ($MEF_1$) when the mice were treated orally with
5 or 10 mg/kg/day of gliotoxin starting 24 hours after infection.
Later, Larin et al. (1965) inferred that dehydrogliotoxin XX and
desthiogliotoxin {XVII, R = R' = H} were, like gliotoxin, active
against poliovirus but, unlike gliotoxin, inactive against measles.
They showed that gliotoxin was active against a series of RNA
virus (poliovirus, HEp strain of rhinovirus, echovirus 28, measles, PR8 strain of influenza A) in culture in monolayers of monkey kidney cells (measles in HEp2). In addition, the Pfizer group
(Larin et al., 1965) was able to demonstrate significant chemotherapeutic effects in monkeys infected with poliovirus, in mice
infected with influenza, and in aerosol influenza infections of dogs.
It has been shown (Larin et al., 1965) that gliotoxin does not inhibit extracellular virus or its adsorption to the infected cell, although little experimental detail was given that would make possible a judgment of the validity of this assertion.

Bacteria. It has been known for more than 25 years that gliotoxin inhibits the growth of bacteria. Waksman and Woodruff

(1942) described its bacteriostatic effect against a wide range of gram-positive organisms. This work has been repeated (Beech and Carr, 1955; Brewer et al., 1965; Brewer et al., 1966a; Brian and Hemming, 1947; Brian and Hemming, 1945; Gilliver, 1946; Heatley and Philpot, 1947; Johnson et al., 1943; Katznelson, 1950; Loewe, 1945; McKee et al., 1943; Nemec et al., 1960; Schatz and Waksman, 1944; Waksman and Geiger, 1944; Waksman and Horning, 1943; Waksman and Reilly, 1945; Wright, 1954) and extended to demonstrate the very high activity against Mycobacteria in vitro (Kavanagh, 1947; Schatz and Waksman, 1944; Tompsett et al., 1950). The antibiotic showed no chemotherapeutic effect in experimental infections of mice with M. tuberculosis H37Rv (Tompsett et al., 1950) or Clostridium perfringens (McKee et al., 1943). An assay based on its inhibition of growth of Bacillus subtilis has been reported (Wright, 1954) and later modified (Brewer et al., 1966a). Despite this work, little is known of the mode of action of gliotoxin. Cavallito and his co-workers (Bailey and Cavallito, 1948; Cavallito and Bailey, 1944; Cavallito et al., 1946) reported that the antibacterial effect of gliotoxin was inhibited in the presence of cysteine and thioglycolic acid, a process capable of reversion by iodometric oxidation, but this result has not been repeated (Dutcher et al., 1945; see also Mason and Kidd, 1951). Indeed, Johnson and his co-workers showed (Dutcher et al., 1945) that all degradation products of gliotoxin including desthiogliotoxin were inactive. This agrees with our results (Table 3) but contrasts with the reported antiviral activity of desthiogliotoxin just discussed. The antibacterial activity of chetomin has been reported by Waksman and his collaborators (Schatz and Waksman, 1944; Waksman and Bugie, 1944; Waksman et al., 1944), who demonstrated that, while it had bactericidal properties with organisms highly sensitive to the antibiotic in vitro, it showed no activity against experimental infections in mice. Most of the results of these antibacterial studies are in agreement except for the question of the concentration at which chetomin inhibits the growth of gram-negative organisms. Differences may be due to the heterogeneous nature of the preparations used. During recent years, we have undertaken a systematic study of the antibacterial action of these disulfides. The similarities in structure between sporidesmin and gliotoxin suggested that the former should inhibit the growth of bacteria although it had not been possible to demonstrate this with crude preparations (Brewer et al., 1966a; Done et al., 1961). In order to compare the relative activities of sporidesmin, chetomin, and gliotoxin, it was essential to define the conditions of the experiment (Brewer et al., 1965; Brewer et al., 1966a). Thus, with an inoculum of about $10^7$ Bacillus subtilis cells, a growth period of 18 hours, and incorporation of the drugs in the medium before inoculation, we obtained the relative activities of chetomin, gliotoxin, and sporidesmin as 1000:100:1. The other

Table 3. Comparative Inhibitions of Growth of <u>Bacillus subtilis</u> (HLX 373) by
3,6-epidithia-2,5-dioxopiperazines (V) and Related Compounds

| Compound Tested | Minimum Concentration in μg ml Inhibiting Growth for 18 hours | Reference to Compound Preparation |
|---|---|---|
| Sporidesmin-B, II, R = R' = H | 400 | Ronaldson et al., 1963 |
| Isosporidesmin-B, XI | 200 | Hodges et al., 1966b |
| Sporidesmin diacetate, II, R = COCH$_3$, R' = OCOCH$_3$ | 120 | Ronaldson et al., 1963 |
| Sporidesmin, II, R = H, R' = OH, benzene complex | 80 | Ronaldson et al., 1963 |
| Sporidesmin-C, XXXV, R = R' = H | - | Hodges et al., 1966a |
| Sporidesmin-C diacetate, XXXV, R = R' = COCH$_3$ | - | Hodges et al., 1966a |
| IX | - | Hodges et al., 1964 |
| X | - | Hodges et al., 1964 |
| Gliotoxin   } XVI, R = R' = H<br>Gliotoxin-B } | 2.0<br>0.8 | Herrmann et al., 1964 |
| Dehydrogliotoxin, XX, R = H | 2.8 | Herrmann et al., 1964; Lowe et al., 1966 |
| Isodehydrogliotoxin, XX, R = H (Position of OH unknown) | 4.0 | A. Taylor, 1966, unpublished work |
| Gliotoxin acetate, XVI, R or R' = COCH$_3$ | 3.0 | Johnson et al., 1953 |
| Dehydrogliotoxin monoacetate, XX, R = COCH$_3$ | 1.0 | Lowe et al., 1966 |
| Gliotoxin dibenzoate, ? XVI, R = R' = COC$_6$H$_5$ | - | Bruce et al., 1944 |
| XXIV | - | Lowe et al., 1966 |
| Dihydro XXIV | - | Lowe et al., 1966 |
| Chetomin, XXXIV, R, R' unknown | 0.08 | Geiger, 1949, D. Brewer, et al., unpublished work |

A dash indicates that normal growth was observed in 1 mg/ml

compounds that are given in Table 3 were then tested with the results shown.  In agreement with previous work (Dutcher et al.,
1945; Mason and Kidd, 1951), gliotoxin dibenzoate was the only
disulfide that was inactive at 1 mg/ml, and all of the degradation
products of sporidesmin and gliotoxin where the disulfide bridge
had been lost were also inactive.  This included the closely related sporidesmin-C XXXV (Figure 7) (Hodges and Shannon, 1966a),
which has a trisulfide bridge but which is otherwise identical to
sporidesmin.  In the course of this work, we noted that the effect
of low concentrations of the disulfides on the growth of the organisms was confined entirely to the lag phase.  With this in mind,

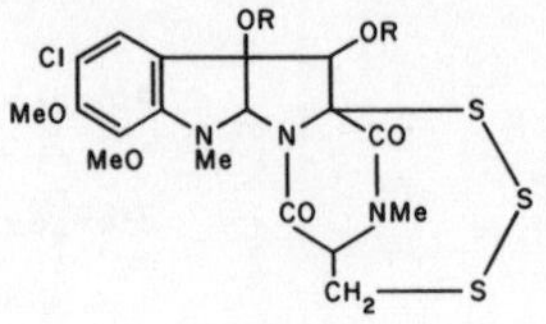

Fig. 7.  Sporidesmin C.

the organisms were grown in a concentration of antibiotic that increased the lag phase by 300 %.  They were then subcultivated at
this concentration until their lag phase of growth was the same as
the parent strain.  By repeating this procedure, cultures of resistant organisms were obtained, and it was found that such organisms
grown in the presence of one of the disulfides were also able to
grow in the presence of others at concentrations that increased
the lag phase of growth of the parent strain by a factor of about
10 (Brewer et al., 1966b).  This demonstration of cross resistance strengthens chemical evidence that the epidithiodioxopipera-
zine ring system is a structural feature of chetomin.  As has been
reported previously (Klimek et al., 1948), these resistant organisms lost their resistance when subcultivated in the absence of a
disulfide.  By using the ability of the disulfides to catalyze the decomposition of azide in the presence of iodine (as described previously), gliotoxin has been determined in the presence of washed
cells (Brewer and Taylor, 1966).

It has been shown that the concentration of gliotoxin in cultures
of Bacillus subtilis decreases faster than in uninoculated controls.
However, if the drug was added before inoculation, the residual
concentration is sufficient to be inhibitory when the cells enter
the logarithmic phase.  Further, resistant cells do not decom-
pose gliotoxin at a rate greater than the parent strain.  They continue to respire in concentrations of gliotoxin that would increase
the lag phase of growth by 48 hours at about the same rate as in
its absence.  Under the experimental conditions used, the respiration rate in the absence of the drug decreases after about 5 hours.
This decrease can be reversed if a source of nitrogen, e.g., am-

monium sulfate, is added. In the presence of gliotoxin, this effect of ammonium sulfate is not observed. We incline to the view that one of the functions of gliotoxin is to inhibit the active transport of certain nutrients into the cell. This is in accord with what is known of the toxicology of sporidesmin in animals.

Fungi. The discovery of gliotoxin came as a result of its ability to inhibit the growth of fungi (Falck, 1931; Haenseler and Allen, 1934; Weindling, 1934; Weindling, 1941), and subsequently these observations have been amply confirmed (Allen et al., 1954; Brian and Hemming, 1947; Dahmen and Moutschen, 1954; Daines, 1937; Diaz-Celayeta, 1962; Di Menna, 1962; Gilliver, 1946; Johnson et al., 1943; Jones and Harper, 1952; Kenner and Murray, 1951; Nemec et al., 1960; Parag, 1961; Pine, 1948; Reilly et al., 1945; van der Laan, 1947; Waksman and Reilly, 1945). It has been shown to inhibit the germination of spores of Botrytis allii (Brian and Hemming, 1945), and this has been used as an assay method for the antibiotic. Some work has been done (Beech and Carr, 1955; Brian and Hemming, 1945; Gregory et al., 1952; Wallen and Skolko, 1951) on its use in the control of fungal infestation of seed, fruit, and vegetables, but the impression one obtains from the literature is that the authors consider simple inorganic chemicals to be more economical. The antifungal effect of gliotoxin in soil has been investigated — a topic closely related to the question of its formation in soil by growing fungi (Evans and Gottlieb, 1955; Jefferys, 1952; Wright, 1954; Wright, 1952) — and it has been shown to be unstable in soils that are not acidic. There is an almost complete absence of knowledge of the mechanism of the antifungal action of these disulfides. Gliotoxin was briefly examined by Kerridge (1958), who found that nucleic acid and protein synthesis were inhibited in Saccharomyces carlsbergensis at concentrations equal to or greater than those causing growth inhibition. There is some dispute concerning the possible antifungal activity of chetomin (Reilly et al., 1945; Tveit and Moore, 1954), which might be resolved by a metabolic transformation of chetomin into an active metabolite in the plant, as discussed previously. No antifungal activity has been reported for sporidesmin.

Mammalian Cell Cultures. The toxicity of gliotoxin to lines of mammalian cells in culture has been reported by several workers to be > 1 µg/ml (Kidd, 1947; Larin et al., 1965; Perlman et al., 1959). Rightsel et al. (1964) found no morphological changes on microscopic examination of monkey kidney cells at 80 to 250 µg/ml, HEp2 cells at 64 µg/ml, and KB cells at 0.45 to 25 µg/ml. Gliotoxin also has inhibitory activity against transplants of Gardner lymphosarcoma in mice (Mason and Kidd, 1951; Reilly et al., 1953), the chemotherapeutic effect being reversed by thiols. Sporidesmin inhibits protein synthesis in HeLa cells and pig kidney cells in discontinuous monolayers at 0.003 µg/ml (Done et al., 1961), its diacetate {II: R = COMe, R' = OCOMe} at 0.006 µg/ml (J. Done, personal communication), and it has been found (D. Perlman, personal communication) that sporidesmin-B {II: R = R' = H} is slightly less toxic than sporidesmin {II: R = H, R' = OH} in the same concentration range against Earle L cells (cf. Perlman et al., 1959), Ehrlich ascites cells, and human and rat pituitary cells. The toxicity of various cell lines to sporidesmin has also been reported by Fastier (1961), who noted that cell lines from rabbit spleen and kidney were about 100 times less sensitive than the cells just described. The effects of sporidesmin on cultures of mammalian cells has been used as a sensitive method for its detection and estimation in crude extracts of plant material (Done et al., 1961; Murphy and Worker, 1960). It is one of the most cytotoxic substances known.

Plants. There are a few reports of the toxicity of these disulfides to plants. Except for slight inhibition of carbonate fixation, little effect was observed when algae (Foter et al., 1953; Tomisek et al., 1957) were treated with gliotoxin. By contrast, necrosis and abnormal mitotic figures have been observed in Allium cepa and Brachythecium rutabulum, both in the plants and in cultures of root, leaf, and stem tissue when treated with gliotoxin concentrations > 10 µg/ml (Dahmen and Moutschen, 1954). The same authors noted a slight chemotherapeutic effect on the invasion of such cultures by pathogenic fungi when they were treated with gliotoxin at 1 to 10 µg/ml. Other phytotoxic effects of gliotoxin (Bastin and van Roey, 1954; Wright, 1951) and of Chaetomium sp. (Winter, 1951) have been reported.

Animals. The toxicity of gliotoxin to mice and rats was reported by Johnson et al. (1943). When mice were given 50 mg/kg orally or intraperitoneally, they died within 24 hours. At half this dose there was a 50% mortality, and hematuria (cf. sporidesmin) was observed in most cases. Recently these results have been confirmed, and it has been shown that mice tolerate a chemotherapeutic program of 5 to 10 mg/kg/day (Larin et al., 1965; Rightsel et al., 1964; Tompsett et al., 1950). Rats are a little more susceptible to sporidesmin (Rimington et al., 1962; Slater and Griffiths, 1963; Slater et al., 1964). A dose of 1 to 5 mg/kg intraperitoneally resulted in a 25% mortality 2 to 8 days after dosing. The pathology of the sporidesmin-intoxicated rat is different in some respects from that of sporidesmin intoxication in sheep and rabbits. Increases in cellular enzymes (e.g., malic dehydrogenase) and cholesterol were observed in the serum of intoxicated rats. When the serum proteins were examined electrophoretically, they also showed an abnormal protein band. Adrenal hyperplasia was observed in the rat as in the sheep. Ascites and/or pleural effusions were common findings in rats treated with doses of sporidesmin > 5 mg/kg, and the transudates contained up to 5 g/100 ml of protein, the electrophoretic characteristics of which were similar to those of the serum proteins. Al-

though the urine of rats treated with sporidesmin has been examined,
no report of hematuria has been made. When sporidesmin was administered to rats intraperitoneally, bile flow ceased after 18 hours
but recommenced at 30 hours and was normal in 3 days. The toxin
had no effect on the conjugation of bilirubin in rats. Thus the pathological changes that occur in rats treated with sporidesmin may
be summarized as a general inflammatory response marked by
ascites and/or pleural effusions, increased capillary permeability
(a property not shown by gliotoxin, T. F. Slater, private communication), and diarrhea.

The young, newly weaned guinea pig was developed in New Zealand as a test animal for the determination of toxicity in pasture
samples (Evans et al., 1957; MacKinnon and Te Punga, 1961;
Perrin, 1957), and this proved to be a reliable though time-con-
suming technique. The assay was applied with success during the
isolation of sporidesmin from cultures of Pithomyces chartarum,
and Synge and White reported (1959) that oral doses of about 2 mg/
kg produced severe liver lesions.

The effect of toxic pasture on New Zealand white rabbits and
some of its chemical pathology were reported shortly after the implication of Pithomyces chartarum in the etiology of facial eczema
(Dodd, 1960; Worker and Dodd, 1960). The results were then compared with the pathological effects of cultures of the fungus (Clare,
1959; Worker and Dodd, 1960). The rabbit is very susceptible to
sporidesmin, 0.5 mg/kg inducing icterus, lipemia, and photosensitization (Mortimer and Taylor, 1966). The inflammatory process
initiated by inserting solutions of sporidesmin into the eyes of rabbits has been used as a rapid method of detecting sporidesmin in
extracts of plant material (Done et al., 1961). Early lipid disfunc-
tion has been studied by Peters (1966). The liver triglyceride fraction increased about threefold and the liver cholesteryl esters by
about 50% after a dose of 1 mg/kg sporidesmin. These increases
were attended by decreased levels of nonesterified fatty acids in
the serum of treated animals. The other classes of serum lipids
were increased. This result is very similar to that observed in
sheep.

The intoxication of sheep with cultures of Pithomyces chartarum
was first demonstrated by Te Punga and MacKinnon (1966). Later,
when adequate quantities of sporidesmin were available, a more detailed investigation of its toxicology was initiated (Done et al., 1962;
Mortimer, 1962; Mortimer, 1963; Mortimer and Taylor, 1962;
Mortimer et al., 1962; Peters, 1963; Peters and Smith, 1964). A
dose of 0.5 to 1 mg/kg orally, subcutaneously, or intravenously induced severe disease. At 1 mg/kg orally, 80% of the dosed animals
died in 24 days, and at 0.5 mg/kg orally, 12% of the animals died in
the same period. Thus the $LD_{50}$ lies between these dose levels. The
clinical response to a single oral dose (Mortimer and Taylor, 1962)
appeared to have two phases. Anorexia and diarrhea were the clin-

ical signs of early intoxication, probably reflecting a general inflammatory response (Gallagher, 1964b) in some ways analogous
to that in the rat.  These conclusions were supported by histolog-
ical (Mortimer, 1963) and postmortem examination.  Examination
of frozen sections of liver revealed the presence of free lipid within the hepatic cells; similar observations had been made earlier
in the case of mice dosed with extracts of toxic grass (Worker,
1959).  The sheep livers were extracted, and it was shown that
there was an increase in the neutral lipid fraction as compared
with similar fractions from normal sheep (Mortimer et al., 1962).
Part of the increase in the neutral lipid fraction was due to the
steroid component (Mortimer et al., 1962; Peters, 1966).  This
phenomenon was later investigated in detail when it was shown
that the principal lipid fraction increased was the triglycerides
(Peters, 1963; Peters and Smith, 1964).  This early liver dis-
function, typified by the accumulation of intrahepatic lipid, is
similar in this respect to that observed after intoxication of animals with many other hepatotoxins, e.g., ethionine and carbon
tetrachloride.  It was also indicated by the failure of animals to
clear bromsulfalein from the circulation (Mortimer, 1962) at this
stage of the intoxication process and perhaps by transient increases
in the levels of intracellular enzymes, e.g., glutamic-oxalacetic
transaminase (Done et al., 1962).  Despite this work, many obvious biochemical problems remain: the pharmacology of sporidesmin is unknown; the biochemical nature of the lesions in the walls
of blood vessels, e.g., in the urinary bladder, is unknown; and it
is not known whether the accumulation of lipid occurs because of
the inability of the liver to synthesize the carrier proteins, as has
been suggested in the case of carbon tetrachloride intoxication, or
whether it is due to some other abnormality.  Four or five days
after dosing, the animals appeared to recover, but they relapsed
at about the tenth day.  At this point many animals became photo-
sensitive, although the nature of the photosensitizing agent is unknown.  The animals were icteric, with high serum levels of bilirubin, steroids, and phospholipids (Done et al., 1962).  There
was present in the serum greatly increased levels of a thermola-
bile lipoprotein, and some of the properties of this material have
been described (Taylor, 1966).  It was shown that the esterified
steroids in the serum were not greatly elevated and the increase was mainly due to the sterol fraction (Done et al., 1962).
Because it is known that intracellular steroids are mostly unes-
terified, and this is certainly true as far as sheep liver is concerned (Peters and Smith, 1964), this increase in sterols in the
circulating fluids is evidence for leakage of cell contents into the
circulating fluids.  Details of the postmortem examinations of
animals at this and later stages of the intoxication process have
been given together with a comprehensive account of the histology
of the disease process (Mortimer, 1963; Mortimer and Taylor,

1962). Very little information is available on possible modifications of the intoxication chemotherapeutically, except for a recent report (Peters and Mortimer, 1966) that a beneficial effect is observed when sheep are treated with cholestyramine.

The toxicity of gliotoxin in primates (Macaca mulatta, Cereopithecus aethiops and Papio cynocephalus) has been studied (Larin et al., 1965). The monkeys were found to tolerate a dose of 0.2 mg/kg given intramuscularly for 15 consecutive days, although some reactions were observed at the site of inoculation. Larin and his co-workers showed the presence of antiviral activity in serum obtained 40 minutes after inoculation, but very low levels were present after 18 hours. Similar antibacterial activities in mouse serum had been reported previously (Tompsett et al., 1950).

## Conclusion

It has been shown that epidithiadioxopiperazines exert growth-inhibitory activity on a wide range of tissues. The possibility of synthesizing novel disulfides on the chance that they will have useful therapeutic properties should be actively pursued. However, my purpose, in conclusion, is rather to draw attention to some of the more disturbing possibilities that emerge from the work done so far. Little is known of the mechanism of biosynthesis of these materials and less of the genetic control of their production. They are produced by genetically variable organisms, and it is possible that other products will be produced in the future with important agricultural implications. Apart from the loss of animals by intoxication with the bizarre metabolites of the microfungi, other somewhat more subtle consequences have to be considered. There is some evidence that these disulfides are translocated by pasture plants and therefore consumed in low concentration by ruminants. The effects of the process on the rumen bacteria are unknown, but if their activity is reduced, the growth rate and possibly the health of the animals will be impaired. The chance colonization of a district with, say, an efficient producer of chetomin could therefore impair the usefulness of the area for animal production.

## Acknowledgments

I wish to thank my colleagues Dr. E. G. Young and Dr. L. C. Vining for reading and correcting the manuscript and Miss D. Hannah for help with the literature review.

## References

Ali, M. S., J. S. Shannon, and A. Taylor, 1966. Unpublished data.

Ali, M. S., and A. Taylor, 1966. Unpublished data.

Allen, R. E., R. S. Shelton, and M. G. Van Campen, 1954, J. Amer. Chem. Soc., 76, 1158.

Argoudelis, A. D., and R. R. Herr, Antimicrobial Agents Chemotherapy, 1962, 780 (Pub. 1963).

Asheshov, I. N., F. Strelite, and E. Hall, 1949, Brit. J. Exp. Pathol., 30, 175.

Bailey, J. H., and C. J. Cavallito, 1948, J. Bacteriol., 55, 175.

Bastin, R., and G. van Roey, 1954, J. Pharm. Belg., 9, 112.

Beech, F. W., and J. G. Carr, 1955, J. Gen. Microbiol., 12, 85.

Beecham, A. F., J. Fridrichsons, and A. McL. Mathieson, 1966, Tetrahedron Letters, 3131.

Beecham, A. F., and A. McL. Mathieson, 1966, Tetrahedron Letters, 3139.

Bell, M. R., Ph.D. Thesis, Cornell University, 1956.

Bell, M. R., J. R. Johnson, B. S. Wildi, and R. B. Woodward, 1958, J. Amer. Chem. Soc., 80, 1001.

Berger, J., E. R. La Sala, W. E. Scott, B. R. Meltsner, L. H. Sternbach, S. Kaiser, S. Teitel, E. Mach, and M. W. Goldberg, 1957, Experientia, 13, 434.

Betina, V., and Z. Baruth, 1964, J. Antibiotics (Tokyo) Ser. A., 17, 127.

Betina, V., P. Nemec, J. Balan, and S. Kovac, 1961, Chem. Zvesti, 15, 843.

Bijvoet, J. M., A. F. Peerdeman, and A. J. van Bommel, 1951, Nature, 168, 271.

Bolhofer, W. A., R. A. Machlowitz, and J. Charney, 1953, Antibiot. Chemotherapy, 3, 382.

Bracken, A., and H. Raistrick, 1947, Biochem. J., 41, 569.

Brewer, D., D. E. Hannah, and A. Taylor, 1965, J. Gen. Microbiol., 39, v.

Brewer, D., D. E. Hannah, and A. Taylor (1966a), Can. J. Microbiol., 12, 1187.

Brewer, D., D. E. Hannah, and A. Taylor, 1966b. Unpublished data.

Brewer, D., and A. Taylor, 1966. Unpublished data.

Brian, P. W., 1944, Nature, 154, 667.

Brian, P. W., 1946a, Brit. Mycol. Soc. Trans., 29, 173.

Brian, P. W., 1946b, Ibid., 29, 211.

Brian, P. W., and H. G. Hemming, 1947, J. Gen. Microbiol.,
1, 158.

Brian, P. W., and H. G. Hemming, 1945, Ann. Appl. Biol.,
32, 214.

Brook, P. J., 1959, New Zealand, J. Agr. Res., 2, 690.

Brook, P. J., 1963, New Zealand, J. Agr. Res., 6, 147.

Brook, P. J., 1964, Ibid., 7, 87.

Brook, P. J., and R. E. F. Matthews, 1960, New Zealand,
J. Sci., 3, 591.

Brook, P. J., and E. V. Mutch, 1964, New Zealand, J. Agr.
Res., 7, 138.

Brookes, P., R. J. Clark, A. T. Fuller, M. P. V. Mijovic,
and J. Walker, 1960a, J. Chem. Soc., 916.

Brookes, P., R. J. Clark, B. Majhofer, M. P. V. Mijovic,
and J. Walker, 1960b, J. Chem. Soc., 925.

Brookes, P., A. T. Fuller, and J. Walker, 1957, J. Chem.
Soc., 689.

Brown, R., 1956, N. Y. State Dept. Health, Ann. Rept. Div.
Labs. and Research, p. 18.

Brown, R., and E. L. Hazen, 1953, Antibiot. Chemotherapy, 3,
818.

Bruce, W. F., J. D. Dutcher, J. R. Johnson, and L. L. Miller,
1944, J. Amer. Chem. Soc., 66, 614.

Cavallito, C. J., and J. H. Bailey, 1944, Science, 100, 390.

Cavallito, C. J., J. H. Bailey, and W. F. Warner, 1946, J.
Amer. Chem. Soc., 68, 715.

Clare, N. T., 1952, "Photosensitization in Diseases of Domestic
Animals," p. 24, Commonwealth Agricultural Bureau,
Farnham Royal, England.

Clare, N. T., 1955, Ad. Vet. Sci., 2, 182.

Clare, N. T., 1959, New Zealand J. Agr. Res., 2, 1249.

Clare, N. T., 1963, New Zealand J. Sci., 6, 429.

Clare, N. T., and J. M. Gumbley, 1962, New Zealand J. Agr.
Res., 5, 36.

Clare, N. T., and P. H. Mortimer, 1964, New Zealand J. Agr. Res., 7, 258.

Corbaz, R., L. Ettlinger, E. Gaümann, W. Keller-Schierlein, F. Kradolfer, L. Neipp, V. Prelog, P. Reusser, and H. Zähner, 1957, Helv. Chim. Acta, 40, 199.

Corey, E. J., and E. Block, 1966, J. Org. Chem., 31, 1663.

Cram, D. J., O. Theander, H. Jager, and M. K. Stanfield, 1963, J. Amer. Chem. Soc., 85, 1430.

Crawley, W. E., P. H. Mortimer, and J. D. Smith, 1961, New Zealand J. Agr. Res., 4, 552.

Cunningham, I. J., 1958, New Zealand J. Agr. Res., 1, 489.

Cunningham, I. J., C. S. M. Hopkirk, and J. F. Filmer, 1942, New Zealand J. Sci. Technol., A24, 185.

Dahl, W. E., and H. L. Pardue, 1965, Anal. Chem., 37, 1382.

Dahmen, M., and J. Moutschen, 1954, Ann. Inst. Pasteur, 87, 204.

Daines, R. H., 1937, Amer. Potato J., 26, 85.

Dean, B. M., M. P. V. Mijovic, and J. Walker, 1961, J. Chem. Soc., 3394.

Diaz-Celayeta, F., 1962, Farmacognosia (Madrid), 22, 75.

Di Menna, M. E., 1962, J. Gen. Microbiol., 27, 249.

Dingley, J. M., 1962, New Zealand J. Agr. Res., 5, 49.

Dingley, J. M., J. Done, A. Taylor, and D. W. Russell, 1962, J. Gen. Microbiol., 29, 127.

Dodd, D. C., 1960, New Zealand J. Agr. Res., 3, 491.

Done, J., P. H. Mortimer, and A. Taylor, 1960, Res. Vet. Sci., 1, 76.

Done, J., P. H. Mortimer, and A. Taylor, 1962, Res. Vet. Sci., 3, 161.

Done, J., P. H. Mortimer, A. Taylor, and D. W. Russell, 1961, J. Gen. Microbiol., 26, 207.

Dutcher, J. D., J. R. Johnson, and W. F. Bruce, 1944a, J. Amer. Chem. Soc., 66, 617.

Dutcher, J. D., J. R. Johnson, and W. F. Bruce, 1944b, J. Amer. Chem. Soc., 66, 619.

Dutcher, J. D., J. R. Johnson, and W. F. Bruce, 1945, J. Amer. Chem. Soc., 67, 1736.

Dutcher, J. D., and A. Kjaer, 1951, J. Amer. Chem. Soc., 73, 4139.

Elvidge, J. A., and F. S. Spring, 1949a, J. Chem. Soc., 2935.

Elvidge, J. A., and F. S. Spring, 1949b, J. Chem. Soc., 5135.

Evans, E., and D. Gottlieb, 1955, Soil Sci., 80, 295.

Evans, J. V., D. McFarlane, C. S. W. Reid, and D. D. Perrin, 1957, New Zealand J. Sci. Technol., A38, 491, 680.

Falck, R., 1931, Mitt. Forstl. Forsch. Schwed., 480.

Fastier, L. B., 1961, New Zealand J. Agr. Res., 4, 72.

Filmer, J. F., 1951, Proc. Specialists Conf. Agric., Adelaide, H.M.S.O., London, p. 320.

Finch, N., C. W. Gemenden, Iva Hsiu-Chu Hsu, and W. I. Taylor, 1963, J. Amer. Chem. Soc., 85, 1520.

Foter, M. J., C. M. Palmer, and T. E. Maloney, 1953, Antibiot. Chemotherapy, 3, 505.

Fridrichsons, J., and A. McL. Mathieson, 1962, Tetrahedron Letters, 1265.

Fridrichsons, J., and A. McL. Mathieson, 1963, Acta Cryst., 16, 1075.

Fridrichsons, J., and A. McL. Mathieson, 1965, Acta Cryst., 18, 1043.

Fuller, A. T., 1955, Nature, 175, 722.

Gallagher, C. H., 1964a, Biochem. Pharmacol., 13, 1017.

Gallagher, C. H., 1964b, Nature, 201, 1293.

Geiger, W. B., 1949, Arch. Biochem. Biophys., 21, 125.

Geiger, W. B., J. E. Conn, and S. A. Waksman, 1944, J. Bacteriol., 48, 531.

Gilliver, K., 1946, Ann. Botany London, 10, 271.

Gilruth, J. G., 1908, New Zealand Dep. Agr. Ann. Rep., 16, 189.

Glister, G. A., and T. I. Williams, 1944, Nature, 153, 651.

Gregory, K. F., O. N. Allen, A. J. Riker, and W. H. Peterson, 1952, Am. J. Botany, 39, 405.

Gregory, P. H., and M. E. Lacey, 1964, Brit. Mycol. Soc. Trans., 47, 25.

Haenseler, C. M., and M. C. Allen, 1934, Phytopathology, 24, 10.

Hall, E. A., F. Kavanagh, and I. N. Asheshov, 1951, Antibiot. Chemotherapy, 1, 369.

Hanson, F. R. and T. E. Eble, 1949, J. Bacteriol., 58, 527.

Harper, L. R., Ph.D. Thesis, Cornell University, 1954.

Heatley, N. G., and H. M. Doery, 1951, Biochem. J., 50, 247.

Heatley, N. G., B. K. Kelly, and N. Smith, 1952, J. Gen. Microbiol., 6, 30.

Heatley, N. G., and F. J. Philpot, 1947, J. Gen. Microbiol., 1, 232.

Herrmann, H., R. Hodges, and A. Taylor, 1964, J. Chem. Soc., 4315.

Hinuma, Y., S. Hamada, T. Yashima, and K. Ishihara, 1955, J. Antibiotics Ser. A 8, 118.

Hodges, R., J. W. Ronaldson, J. S. Shannon, A. Taylor, and E. P. White, 1964, J. Chem. Soc., 26.

Hodges, R., J. W. Ronaldson, A. Taylor, and E. P. White, 1963a, Chem. Ind. (London), 42.

Hodges, R., J. W. Ronaldson, A. Taylor, and E. P. White, 1963b, J. Chem. Soc., 5332.

Hodges, R., and J. S. Shannon, 1966a, Australian J. Chem., 19, 1059.

Hodges, R., J. S. Shannon, and A. Taylor, 1966b, J. Chem. Soc., 1803.

Hodges, R., and A. Taylor, 1964, J. Chem. Soc., 4310.

Hore, D. E., 1960, Australian Vet. J., 36, 172.

Hull, R. N., and J. M. Lavelle, 1953, Proc. Soc. Exp. Biol. Med., 83, 787.

Janes, B. S., 1959, Nature, 184, 1327.

Jefferys, E. G., 1952, J. Gen. Microbiol., 7, 295.

Johnson, J. R., 1955, "The Structure of Gliotoxin," in The Roger Adams Symposium, John Wiley & Sons, Inc., New York, pp. 60-90.

Johnson, J. R., and J. M. Andreen, 1950, J. Amer. Chem. Soc., 72, 2862.

Johnson, J. R., W. F. Bruce, and J. D. Dutcher, 1943, J. Amer. Chem. Soc., 65, 2005.

Johnson, J. R. and J. B. Buchanan, 1951, J. Amer. Chem. Soc., 73, 3749.

Johnson, J. R., and J. B. Buchanan, 1953, J. Amer. Chem. Soc., 75, 2103.

Johnson, J. R., R. B. Hasbrouck, J. D. Dutcher, and W. F. Bruce, 1945, J. Amer. Chem. Soc., 67, 423.

Johnson, J. R., A. R. Kidwai, and J. S. Warner, 1953, J. Amer. Chem. Soc., 75, 2110.

Johnson, J. R., A. A. Larsen, A. A. Holley, and K. Gerzon, 1947, J. Amer. Chem. Soc., 69, 2364.

Johnson, J. R., W. C. McCrone, and W. F. Bruce, 1944, J. Amer. Chem. Soc., 66, 501.

Jones, A. H., and G. S. Harper, 1952, Food Technol., 6, 304.

Katagiri, K., and K. Sato, 1961, J. Antibiotics (Japan) Ser. B 14, 15.

Katagiri, K. and K. Sugiura, 1961 (Pub. 1962), Antimicrobial Agents Chemotherapy, 162.

Katznelson, H., 1950, J. Bacteriol., 59, 471.

Kavanagh, F., 1947, J. Bacteriol., 54, 761.

Kelly, B. K., G. A. Miller, and C. W. Hale, 1952, J. Gen. Microbiol., 6, 41.

Kenner, B. A., and F. J. Murray, 1951, Antibiot. Chemotherapy, 1, 509.

Kerridge, D., 1958, J. Gen. Microbiol., 19, 497.

Kidd, J. G., 1947, Science, 105, 511.

Klimek, J. W., C. J. Cavallito, and J. H. Bailey, 1948, J. Bacteriol., 55, 139.

Komatsu, N., S. Nakazawa, M. Hamada, M. Shimo, and T. Tomosugi, 1959, J. Antibiotics (Japan) Ser. A 12, 12.

Lacey, M. E., and P. H. Gregory, 1962, Nature, 193, 85.

Larin, N. M., P. Copping, R. H. Herbst-Laier, B. Roberts, and R. B. M. Wenham, 1965, Chemotherapia, 10, 12.

Lautenschlaeger, F., 1966, J. Org. Chem., 31, 1679.

Lloyd, A. B., and R. T. J. Clarke, 1959, New Zealand J. Agr. Res., 2, 1084.

Loewe, H., 1945, Deut. Apotheker-Z., 60, 25.

Lowe, G., A. Taylor, and L. C. Vining, 1966, J. Chem. Soc., 1799.

McFarlane, D., J. V. Evans, and C. S. W. Reid, 1959, New Zealand J. Agr. Res., 2, 194.

McKee, C. M., D. M. Hamre, and G. Rake, 1943, Proc. Soc. Exp. Biol. Med., 54, 211.

MacKinnon, M. M., and W. A. Te Punga, 1961, New Zealand J. Agr. Res., 4, 141.

Marbrook, J., 1964, New Zealand J. Agr. Res., 7, 596.

Marbrook, J., and R. E. F. Matthews, 1962, New Zealand J. Agr. Res., 5, 223.

Margalith, P., G. Beretta, and M. T. Timbal, 1959, Antibiot. Chemotherapy, 9, 71.

Mason, J. W., and J. G. Kidd, 1951, J. Immunol., 66, 99.

Menzel, A. E. O., O. Wintersteiner, and J. C. Hoogerheide, 1944, J. Biol. Chem., 152, 419.

Mijovic, M. P. V., and J. Walker, 1960, J. Chem. Soc., 909.

Mijovic, M. P. V., and J. Walker, 1961, Ibid., 3381.

Mitchell, K. J., R. G. Thomas, and R. T. J. Clarke, 1961, New Zealand J. Agr. Res., 4, 566.

Mitchell, K. J., T. O. Walshe, and N. G. Robertson, 1959, New Zealand J. Agr. Res., 2, 584.

Mortimer, P. H., 1962, Res. Vet. Sci., 3, 269.

Mortimer, P. H., 1963, Res. Vet. Sci., 4, 166.

Mortimer, P. H., and A. Taylor, 1962, Res. Vet. Sci., 3, 147.

Mortimer, P. H., and A. Taylor, 1966. Unpublished data.

Mortimer, P. H., A. Taylor, and F. B. Shorland, 1962, Nature, 194, 550.

Mull, R. P., R. W. Townley, and C. R. Scholtz, 1945, J. Amer. Chem. Soc., 67, 1626.

Murch, G. V., and P. J. Brook, 1964, New Zealand J. Agr. Res., 7, 129.

Murphy, A. M., and N. A. Worker, 1960, New Zealand J. Agr. Res., 3, 34.

Nagase, M., H. Yamamoto, M. Matsuoka, H. Umesawa, and R. Urahara, 1959, Japan, 6450; Chem. Abs., 54, 831c.

Neill, J. C., 1940, New Zealand J. Sci. Technol., A 21, 280.

Nemec, P., V. Betina, and J. Balan, 1960, Chem. Zvesti, 14, 674.

Ogawa, H., T. Niida, Y. Sekizawa, M. Ogasawara, S. Kondo, and S. Aoki, 1963, Japan, 12, 745; Chem. Abs., 59, 9279f.

Owen, S. P., A. Dietz, and G. W. Camiener, 1962 (Pub. 1963), Antimicrobial Agents Chemotherapy, 772.

Packard, R. Q., 1960, New Zealand J. Sci., 3, 412.

Parag, Y., 1961, Can. J. Microbiol., 7, 838.

Patterson, A. L., 1963, Acta Cryst., 16, 1255.

Percival, J. C., 1959, New Zealand J. Agr. Res., 2, 1041.

Percival, J. C. and R. H. Thornton, 1958, Nature, 182, 1095.

Perlman, D., N. A. Giuffre, P. W. Jackson, and F. E. Giardinello, 1959, Proc. Soc. Exp. Biol. Med., 102, 290.

Perrin, D. D., 1957, New Zealand J. Sci. Technol., A38, 669.

Perrin, D. D., 1959, New Zealand J. Agr. Res., 2, 266.

Perrin, D. D., E. P. White, and N. T. Clare, 1953, Proc. New Zealand Soc. Animal Production, 12, 121.

Peters, J. A., 1963, Nature, 200, 286.

Peters, J. A., 1966, Nature, 210, 601.

Peters, J. A., and P. H. Mortimer, 1966, New Zealand J. Agr. Res., 9, 137.

Peters, J. A., and L. M. Smith, 1964, Biochem. J., 92, 379.

Peterson, S. W., 1955, Nature, 176, 395.

Pine, L., Ph.D. Thesis, University of Wisconsin, Madison, 1948.

Pittillo, R. G., M. Lucas, C. Woolley, R. T. Blackwell, and C. Moncrief, 1965, Nature, 205, 773.

Powell, H. M., C. G. Culbertson, J. M. McGuire, M. M. Hoehn, and L. A. Baker, 1952, Antibiot. Chemotherapy, 2, 432.

Reilly, H. C., A. Schatz, and S. A. Waksman, 1945, J. Bacteriol., 49, 585.

Reilly, H. C., C. C. Stook, and S. M. Buckley, 1953, Cancer Res., 13, 684.

Rhone-Poulenc, S. A., 1963 (Belgium) 614, 211; Chem. Abs., 58, 9601e. (Belgian patent.)

Rhone-Poulenc, S. A., 1965 (France) M2620; Chem. Abs., 62, 4575c.

Rightsel, W. A., H. G. Schneider, B. J. Sloan, P. R. Graf, F. A. Miller, Q. R. Bartz, J. Ehrlich, and E. J. Dixon, 1964, Nature, 204, 1333.

Rimington, C., T. F. Slater, W. G. Spector, U. D. Sträuli,
    and D. A. Willoughby, 1962, Nature, 194, 1152.

Ronaldson, J. W., A. Taylor, E. P. White, and R. J. Abraham,
    1963, J. Chem. Soc., 3172.

Ross, D. J., 1960a, New Zealand J. Sci., 3, 15.

Ross, D. J., 1960b, Ibid., 3, 441.

Ross, D. J., 1962, New Zealand J. Sci., 5, 246.

Ross, D. J. and R. H. Thornton, 1962, New Zealand J. Sci., 5,
    165.

Russell, D. W., R. L. M. Synge, A. Taylor, and E. P. White,
    1962, J. Chem. Soc., 554.

Russell, G. R., 1960, Nature, 186, 788.

Russell, G. R., 1962, Nature, 193, 354.

Sandos, J., N. T. Clare, and E. P. White, 1959, New Zealand
    J. Agr. Res., 2, 623.

Schatz, A., and S. A. Waksman, 1944, Proc. Soc. Exp. Biol.
    Med., 57, 244.

Sensi, P., R. Ballotta, and G. G. Gallo, 1959, Antibiot. Chemo-
    therapy, 9, 76.

Shannon, J. S., 1963, Tetrahedron Letters, 801.

Shimo, M., T. Shiga, T. Tomosugi, and I. Kamoi, 1959, J.
    Antibiotics (Japan) Ser. A. 12, 1.

Shimo, M., and T. Tomosugi, 1960 (Japan), 15,450; Chem.
    Abs., 55, 15830a.

Shionogi & Co., Ltd., 1964 (Britain) 961,262; Chem. Abs., 61,
    11298d.

Simpson, J. E. V., D. P. Sinclair, J. B. Swan, and J. F.
    Filmer, 1957, New Zealand J. Sci. Technol., A38, 947.

Sinclair, D. P., 1961, New Zealand J. Agr. Res., 4, 492.

Slater, T. F., and A. L. Greenbaum, 1965, Biochem. J., 96,
    484.

Slater, T. F., A. L. Greenbaum, and D. Y. Wang, 1963,
    "Lysosomes," Ciba Foundation Symposium, Churchill, London.

Slater, T. F., and D. B. Griffiths, 1963, Biochem. J., 88, 60P.

Slater, T. F., U. Sträuli, and B. Sawyer, 1964, Res. Vet. Sci.,
    5, 450.

Slechta, L., 1965 (Pub. 1966), Antimicrobial Agents and Chemo-
    therapy, 326.

Smith, J. D., and W. E. Crawley, 1962, New Zealand J. Agr.
    Res., 5, 183.

Smith, J. D., and W. E. Crawley, 1964, New Zealand J. Agr.
    Res., 7, 281.

Smith, J. D., W. E. Crawley, and F. T. Lees, 1961a, New
    Zealand J. Agr. Res., 4, 538.

Smith, J. D., W. E. Crawley, and F. T. Lees, 1961b, New
    Zealand J. Agr. Res., 4, 725.

Smith, J. D., W. E. Crawley, and F. T. Lees, 1962a, New
    Zealand J. Agr. Res., 5, 22.

Smith, J. D., W. E. Crawley, and F. T. Lees, 1962b, New
    Zealand J. Agr. Res., 5, 43.

Smith, J. D., F. T. Lees, and W. E. Crawley, 1963, New
    Zealand J. Agr. Res., 6, 518.

Stanley, N. F., 1944, Australian J. Sci., 6, 151.

Stanley, N. F., and J. A. Mills, 1946, Australian J. Exp. Biol.
    Med. Sci., 24, 133.

Su, T. L., 1948, Brit. J. Exp. Pathol., 29, 473.

Suhadolnik, R. J., and R. G. Chenoweth, 1958, J. Amer. Chem.
    Soc., 80, 4391.

Sumiki, Y., and H. Umezawa, 1960 (Japan) 10,996; Chem. Abs.,
    55, 9780e.

Synge, R. L. M., and E. P. White, 1959, Chem. Ind. (London),
    1546.

Synge, R. L. M., and E. P. White, 1960, New Zealand J. Agr.
    Res., 3, 907.

Taylor, A., 1966. Unpublished data.

Te Punga, W. A., and M. M. MacKinnon, 1966. Unpublished
    data.

Thornton, R. H., 1963a, New Zealand J. Agr. Res., 6, 318.

Thornton, R. H., 1963b, Ibid., 6, 469.

Thornton, R. H., and J. C. Percival, 1959, Nature, 183, 63.

Thornton, R. H., and D. J. Ross, 1959, New Zealand J. Agr.
    Res., 2, 1002.

Thornton, R. H., and D. P. Sinclair, 1960, New Zealand J. Agr. Res., 3, 300.

Thornton, R. H., and W. B. Taylor, 1963, New Zealand J. Agr. Res., 6, 329.

Tomisek, A., M. R. Reid, W. A. Short, and H. E. Skipper, 1957, Plant Physiol., 32, 7.

Tomosugi, T., I. Kamoi, T. Shiga, and M. Shimo, 1959, J. Antibiotics (Japan) Ser. A. 12, 7.

Tompsett, R., W. McDermott, and J. G. Kidd, 1950, J. Immunol., 65, 59.

Tveit, M. T., Acta Pathol. Microbiol. Scand., 1955, 37, 429.

Tveit, M., 1956, Acta Agr. Scand., 6, 13.

Tveit, M., and M. B. Moore, 1954, Phytopathology, 44, 686.

Tveit, M., and R. K. S. Wood, 1955, Ann. Appl. Biol., 43, 538.

Upjohn Co., 1965 (Britain) 974,541; Chem. Abs., 62, 5855d.

van der Laan, P. A., 1947, Tijdschr. Plantenziekten, 53, 180.

Waisvisz, J. M., M. G. van der Hoeven, J. van Peppen, and W. C. M. Zwennis, 1957, J. Amer. Chem. Soc., 79, 4520.

Waksman, S. A., and E. Bugie, 1944, J. Bacteriol., 48, 527.

Waksman, S. A., E. Bugie, and H. S. Reilly, 1944, Bull. Torrey Botan. Club, 71, 107.

Waksman, S. A., and W. B. Geiger, 1944, J. Bacteriol., 47, 391.

Waksman, S. A., and E. S. Horning, 1943, Mycologia, 35, 47.

Waksman, S. A., E. S. Horning, and E. L. Spenser, 1943, J. Bacteriol., 45, 233.

Waksman, S. A., and H. C. Reilly, 1945, Ind. Eng. Chem., Anal. Ed., 17, 556.

Waksman, S. A., and H. B. Woodruff, 1942, J. Bacteriol., 44, 373.

Wallen, V. R., and A. J. Skolko, 1951, Can. J. Botany, 29, 316.

Warner, J. S., Ph.D. Thesis, Cornell University, 1953.

Weil, E. D., K. J. Smith, and R. J. Gruber, 1966, J. Org. Chem., 31, 1669.

Weindling, R., 1932, Phytopathology, 22, 837.

Weindling, R., 1934, Ibid., 24, 1153.

Weindling, R., 1937, Ibid., 27, 1175.

Weindling, R., 1941, Ibid., 31, 991.

Weindling, R., 1938, Botan. Rev., 4, 475.

Weindling, R., and O. H. Emerson, 1936, Phytopathology, 26, 1068.

Weindling, R., and H. S. Faucett, 1936, Hilgardia, 10, 1.

Winstead, J. A., and R. J. Suhadolnik, 1960, J. Amer. Chem. Soc., 82, 1644.

Winter, A. G., 1951, Phytopathol. Z., 18, 221.

White, E. P., 1958a, New Zealand J. Agr. Res., 1, 433.

White, E. P., 1958b, New Zealand J. Agr. Res., 1, 859.

Worker, N. A., 1959, Proc. New Zealand Soc. Animal Production.

Worker, N. A., and D. C. Dodd, 1960, New Zealand J. Agr. Res., 3, 712.

Wright, D. E., and I. T. Forrester, 1965, Can. J. Biochem., 43, 881.

Wright, J. M., 1951, Ann. Botany London, 15, 493.

Wright, J. M., 1952, Nature, 170, 673.

Wright, J. M., 1954, Ann. Appl. Biol., 41, 280.

Yamaguchi, H., Y. Nakayama, K. Takeda, K. Tawara, K. Maeda, T. Takeuchi, and H. Umezawa, 1957, J. Antibiotics (Japan), Ser. A 10, 195.

Yoshida, T., 1962 (Japan) 6349; Chem. Abs., 59, 6956a.

# THE FUROCOUMARINS — A FAMILY OF PHOTOTOXIC COMPOUNDS

Lester D. Scheel, Ph.D.
Department of Health, Education and Welfare
U.S. Public Health Service
Division of Occupational Health
Cincinnati, Ohio

The purpose of the present review of the furocoumarin litera-ture is to define the limits of available knowledge concerning the biological occurrence and the biological effects of this family of compounds. Therefore no pretense toward completeness of the review is made, and none is intended.

## History

Historically, the value of the photodynamic effect of this family of compounds was recognized originally in an herb treatment for leukoderma that dates back before 1400 B.C., as evidenced by writings in the Indian sacred book Atharva Veda (Bloomfield, 1897). Hoernle (1893) in a translation of the Bower manuscript, an old Buddhist writing dating about 200 A.D., found mention of a cure for leukoderma using a poultice application of material from a plant that is now classified as Psoralea corylifolia.

The first furocoumarin to be isolated was 5-methoxy-psoralen in 1834 by Kalbrunner from bergamot oil, and Thomas (1911) com-pared his isolated xanthotoxin to it. The chemical structure of xanthotoxin was synthesized and thus established by Spath and Holzen (1933) in 1933. Other historic aspects concerning the fu-ranocoumarins and their photodynamic effect are reviewed by Fitzpatrick and Pathak (1959) and Fowlks (1959).

As a result of the origin and use of the active plant materials for the treatment of abnormality in skin pigmentation and as a re-sult of the effect of sunlight on the skin pigmentation, it was a nat-ural consequence that the synergistic effect of the furanocoumarins and sunlight on the skin should be observed long before the mecha-nism of this effect was understood. Therefore, in place of the word "photodynamic," we have chosen to use the term "phototoxic" to describe the effects of this coumarin family not only on mamma-

lian skin but also on paramecia, bacteria, and bacteriophage.
The use of the word phototoxic in this paper denotes a combination of a concentration of the compound and exposure to radiant
energy such that cellular damage and/or cellular death will occur. Conversely, under the test conditions in the absence of
either the compound or the radiant exposure, no toxic effect is
observed.

Although there are twelve different ways in which the furan ring
can be condensed with the coumarin molecule, this paper will discuss only two of these because data on the biological activity of
this family of compounds centers around these two naturally occurring forms. The isolated furocoumarins that have been most
thoroughly studied for their biologic effects have been the linear
(2', 3', 6, 7) condensed ring structures, psoralens, and the angular (2', 3', 7, 8) condensed ring structures, the angelicins.

## Nomenclature

In describing the furanocoumarins there are three methods of
numbering listed and used in the literature. In the Indian literature the points of importance in their nomenclature are the following:

1.  All labeling assumes coumarin is the parent molecule, and
the conventional numbering of the ring structure in the clockwise
direction from the hetero atom is followed.

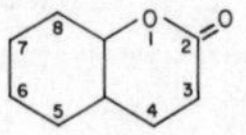

Fig. 1.  Coumarin.

2.  In ring fusion with the coumarin structure, the derivative
ring and the fusion linkage are designated in the naming of the
compound, thus psoralen is furano (6.7, 2, 3) coumarin (Figure 2), and angelicin is furano (7, 8, 4, 5) coumarin (Figure 3).

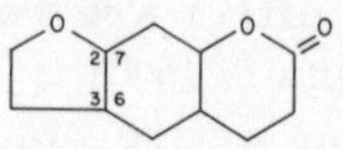

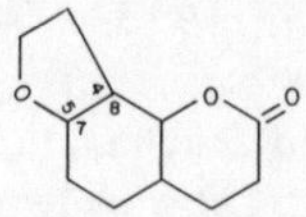

Fig. 2.  Psoralen.          Fig. 3.  Angelicin.

In this country, the Food and Drug Administration (Curtis, 1959)
has chosen to use the same clockwise numbering system from the
hetero atom but has chosen to use prime number designations in

the furan ring systems.  Thus, as indicated by Kaufman (1961), the angular ring system proved by synthesis to condense with the hydroxyl at position 7 on the coumarin ring system for isopsoralens would number the coumarin ring clockwise (Figure 4) and the furan ring counterclockwise (Figure 5).

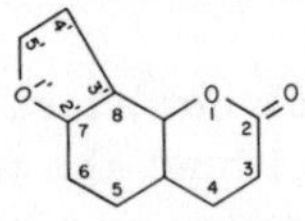

Fig. 4.   Psoralen. 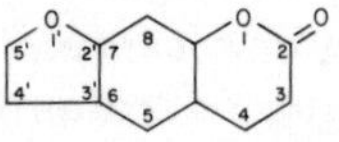          Fig. 5.   Isopsoralen.

In using this numbering system for the psoralens, the designation of the substituents are given by number followed by the suffixes psoralen or isopsoralen.  No indication of ring fusion is given, however.

The third method in use is that described in Chemical Abstracts where the furocoumarins are indexed as follows:

Psoralen = δ-lactone of 6-hydroxy-5-benzofuranacrylic acid.

Isopsoralen = δ-lactone of 4-hydroxy-5-benzofuranacrylic acid.

In addition to the confusion in scientific nomenclature, the common names attached to the herb preparations as well as pseudo-scientific trade names attached to these products by the drug companies are in use in the literature.

## Natural Occurrence

At the present time, naturally occurring coumarin compounds are known to be present in at least 66 different varieties of plants and have been identified as 0.1 to 1.5% of the dry weight in the Orchidacae, Leguminacae, Rutacae, Umbelliferae, and Labiate.

The furocoumarins have been identified in a wide variety of semitropical plants, seeds, and fruits, although little or nothing is known concerning the function of these compounds in the metabolism of the plants (Pathak et al., 1962).  In the symbiotic growth of the mold Sclerotinia sclerotiorum on the celery plant, it has been shown that two furocoumarins are produced by the mold (Perone et al., 1964; Scheel et al., 1963).

## Isolation

The furocoumarins, like coumarins in general, occurred in plant tissue in the free form and conjugated as the glucoside.  The isolation procedures published over the past 100 years have emphasized the lability of the lactone ring systems and have there-

fore generally been most successful when water has been removed
from the plant tissue as the first step. In the very wet celery tissue (Scheel et al., 1963), it was convenient to remove the water
by lyophilizing the tissue, thus achieving the dehydration with a
minimum of concurrent oxidation and at a low temperature over a
relatively short time. This procedure provides a thoroughly de-
hydrated product that is very suitable for the next step, extraction
with a nonpolar solvent.

In choosing petroleum ether for the solvent extraction, the ob-
ject was to remove the organic matter without the possibility of
substitution or reaction. Again this step was performed at room
temperature with repeated solvent applications (2 times) to ensure
complete extraction.

The concentration of the extract was accomplished by evaporation at room temperature under reduced pressure and with a small
stream of air to ebullate the mixture and prevent bumping. The
4, 5', 8 trimethylpsoralen and 8-methoxypsoralen crystallized out
of the concentrated extract leaving the plant pigments in solution.
The microscopic examination of the crystals indicated at least two
different crystals present in the filtered product. Following solvent trials, the crystals were separated by dissolving the mixed
crystals in hot absolute methanol, and on cooling the 4, 5', 8 trimethylpsoralen crystallized and the 8-methoxypsoralen remained
in solution. After removing the trimethylpsoralen, the filtrate
was diluted with 2 volumes of cold water and placed in the refrigerator where the 8-methoxypsoralen slowly crystallized from the
mixed solvent. In general, the design of the isolation process attempted to treat the extractables as gently as possible and prevent
the interaction of the coumarin ring system with the solvents.

Kuske (1938) stimulated interest in this family of compounds as
a result of the isolation and identification of three furocoumarins
from plant material and their association with lesions of the contaminated skin following exposure to sunlight. This interest was
stimulated further when in 1941 Fahmy started work at the University of Cairo on a preparation used by Egyptian herb doctors
to treat cases of leukoderma. By 1947 their group had isolated
three active crystalline compounds (Fahmy and Abu-Shady, 1947)
and tested them with encouraging results.

## Synthesis

This interest became manifest in the synthetic efforts of organic
chemists when the group of chemists working at the University of
Delhi (Gupta and Seshadri, 1953) reported their synthesis of several dihydrofuranocoumarins. This group has remained active in
the synthesis of this type of compound and has reported a general
method for synthesis of linear (psoralens) furocoumarins (Seshadri
and Sood, 1963). This synthesis (Figure 6) involves starting with

5-allyl-4-hydroxy-2-methoxy benzaldehyde, which is condensed
with sodium acetate to form 6-allyl-7-hydroxy coumarin, which
is then oxidized with osmium tetroxide and potassium perchlorate
or ozone to remove a carbon from the allyl side chain. The furan
ring closure is accomplished by warming with polyphosphoric acid
to give a 36% yield of psoralen. This synthesis has the advantage
that no blocking groups are necessary for the reactive 3, 4, 5,
and 8 positions in the coumarin portion of the molecule. The removal of the carbon atom from the allyl group before ring closure
makes possible the formation of the furan ring without substituents
in the 4' or 5' positions on the furan ring.

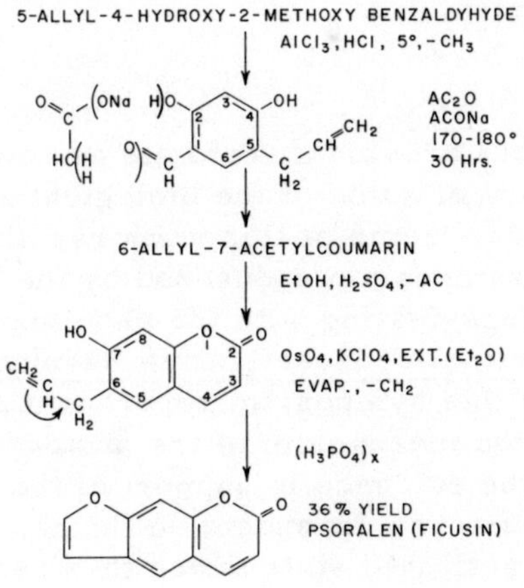

Fig. 6.  Synthesis of psoralen (Seshadri and Sood, 1963).

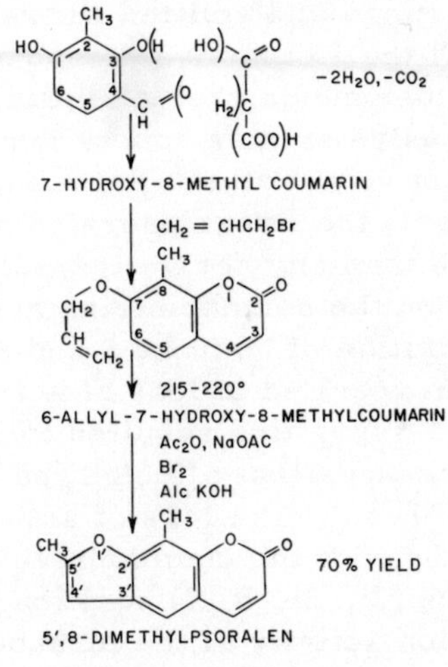

Fig. 7.  Synthesis of methylpsoralens (Kaufman, 1961).

Kaufman (1961) devised a method for synthesis of methylated psoralens (Figure 7) by condensation of malonic acid with 4-formyl-2-methylresorcinal under conditions described by Vorsatz (1936) to give 7-hydroxy-8-methyl coumarin-3-carboxylic acid, which, on warming, lost $CO_2$ to give a 70% yield of 7-hydroxy-8-methylcoumarin. By treating the 7-hydroxy compound with allyl bromide, the 7-allyloxy-8-methyl coumarin is formed; this, when heated, rearranges to form 6-allyl-7-hydroxy-8-methylcoumarin. The compound is then acetylated to reduce bromination of the ring when bromine is added to the allyl double bond. Following bromination of the double bond, the furan ring closure is accomplished with reflux in alcoholic KOH to yield 5'-8-dimethylpsoralen.

## Biological Action

These two methods provide a versatile armament for the synthesis and evaluation of some of the biological actions of this family of compounds. Some of this work has already begun and was reported at a symposium sponsored by the Upjohn Company in 1958. Proceedings dealing with the phototoxic effect were published in the Journal of Investigative Dermatology (Curtis, 1959). Included in this symposium report is a paper by Fowlks (1959) concerning the mechanism of the photodynamic effect in which he reviews the evidence in support of the hypothesis that the photodynamic effect is dependent on the absorption of light energy to form an activated state which then reacts with the biological system. With respect to the furocoumarin compounds, Pathak and Fellman (1960, 1961) reported on 37 compounds and found that of 21 biologically active compounds 20 were activated in the 340 to 380 mμ range and emitted fluorescence in the 420 to 460 mμ region. Of the 16 inactive compounds included in the study, only 2 of the compounds gave a similar spectral response.

As a result of extensive studies concerning molecular structure and erythemal activity, Pathak, Fellman, and Kaufman (1960) have established that (1) the linear psoralen nucleus is equal to or more highly active than any derivative; (2) substitution at both the 3 and 4 positions on the coumarin ring system resulted in loss of activity; (3) substitution of both the 5 and 8 position on the coumarin ring system resulted in loss of activity; (4) substitution in both the 4' and 5' position resulted in loss of activity; (5) other structural changes that affected the resonance of the psoralen ring system resulted in loss of activity; (6) the condensation of the furan ring with the coumarin ring structure in any position other than the (2', 3', 6, 7) position is inactive, as indicated by the radiation activity of the furanocoumarin erythema test.

The method of bioassay for this type of reaction devised by Pathak and Fitzpatrick (1959) has given reproducible results re-

gardless of the animal species used. In addition to the studies
concerned with the phototoxic response obtained in the skin of
animals, the work of Pathak and Fellman (1960) using enzyme
solutions (lactic and succinic dehydrogenase and cytochrome oxi-
dase) indicated that the radiation of the furocoumarin caused the
formation of a triplet stage of psoralen that interacted with radiation-induced free radicals in the protein structure and stabilized
the altered protein structure. This work suggests that the furanocoumarins act as an adjunct to radiation denaturation of the
protein structure based on interaction with radiation-induced al-
terations in the protein structure.

In other work on the mechanism of action of these compounds,
El-Mofty et al. (1959) have studied the effect of orally administered 8-methoxypsoralen on the copper and glutathione levels of
blood and liver in rats. Using adrenalectomized animals, they
showed that the effect on the blood level of copper was not mediated via adrenal stimulation but must have been due to a stimulating effect mediated through the pituitary gland because the effect
of the drug on copper mobilization was abolished in hypophesec-
tomized animals but was not abolished in adrenalectomized animals.

These observations are highly significant because they indicate
a central hormonal control over copper binding in the body structures and in addition provide evidence that this family of organic
compounds can produce striking biological effects with or without
associated radiation synergism.

The synergistic action of radiation and the furocoumarins has
been repeatedly demonstrated and is operative whether the compounds are applied topically or are given orally. However, if the
radiation exposure is not applied within the first 3 to 4 hours after the administration of the compound, no synergistic activity
is found. Therefore the absorption and inactivation of the furocoumarins in response to the radiation effect is fairly rapid. In
spite of these natural safeguards, the very high toxic potential of
this synergistic action has produced disease problems (Birmingham et al., 1961) and should be kept in mind when sunlight and
dermatologic reactions are observed.

From a toxicologic point of view, the activity of the psoralens
under the standard assay varies to some extent with the species
of animal used. In the guinea pig, using the skin erythema test,
4, 5', 8-trimethylpsoralen gives a positive reaction when 2.5 µg/
in.$^2$ of skin is applied and exposed to radiation (Pathak and Fitzpatrick, 1959). In rabbits under the same experimental conditions, 0.1 µg of the 4, 5', 8-trimethylpsoralen/in.$^2$ produces a
similar positive erythema reaction (Perone et al., 1964). In general, the experience of the Dermatology Laboratory of the Division of Occupational Health indicates that rabbit skin is more sensitive to primary irritation than human skin.

In yet another way the furanocoumarins are implicated as biologically active compounds, as shown by the studies reported by Khadzhai and Kuznetsova (1962). In their studies with 8-isopentyloxypsoralen (imperatorin, ammidin) they were able to show that this compound has a spasmolytic effect about equal on a dose basis to that of papaverine. In addition, it has a relatively low photosensitizing activity and low toxicity. The arterial pressure decreased, but the respiration and heart rate were not affected. In other studies on the isolated rabbit heart with a mixture (1:1) of 8-methoxypsoralen and 5-methoxypsoralen they showed that 10 ppm of the compounds lowers arterial pressure and smooth muscle tonus, stimulates the rhythm, and decreases the amplitude of the heart (Khadzhai and Kuznetsova, 1963).

To date, no studies concerned with absorption, excretion, acute, or chronic toxicity by any route of administration to animals have been found in the literature. Liver function studies on humans receiving 30 mg oral doses of 8-methoxypsoralen revealed no significant changes in the bromsulphalein, thymol, zinc turbidity, and cephalincholesterol tests (Labby et al., 1959; Tucker, 1959). The only adverse clinical observations reported were occasional periods of epigastric distress, vertigo, and nausea (Hoe Kenga, 1959).

Although the main studies reported in this review have been concerned with the phototoxic response of mammalian skin, it should be made clear that other studies in the literature provide evidence of other biological activities of the furocoumarins. Rodighiero (1954) has shown that psoralen, 8-methoxypsoralen, and angelicin inhibit seed germination, root growth, and seedling growth. In addition, the same group observed that $5.0 \times 10^{-5}$ M solutions of psoralen or 5-methoxypsoralen induced a 40% mitosis with chromosome mutations in onion root tips during a 4-hour incubation at 20°C (Musajo, 1955). At higher concentrations there was total inhibition of mitosis.

In studies reported by Chakraborty, Das Gupta, and Bose (1957), it was shown that psoralen and 8-isopentyloxypsoralen (imperatorin ammidin) were the most effective antifungal agents tested. It is interesting to speculate that compounds of this type are perhaps nature's way of controlling fungus growth in the tropical areas of the world.

In summary, the furanocoumarins are a family of compounds whose synergistic action in combination with radiant energy of the 340 to 380 mμ region is maximum in the simple or unsubstituted form, as indicated by the erythema reaction, following either topical or oral administration in animals and man. These compounds occur in various tropical and semitropical plants and in at least one case have been strongly indicated to be the product of mold growth in plant tissue.

Although the action of furocoumarins in association with ultraviolet radiation constitute an important biological phenomenon,
the observation that this family of compounds can cause mobilization of copper ions from the liver to the blood, an action that has
been shown to be mediated directly through the pituitary gland, is
another striking example of the biological activity of this family
of compounds and should be studied further.  At the present time
there is no evidence to connect the effect on copper caused by the
furocoumarins with the spasmolytic effect of these compounds on
smooth muscle that has also been observed; however, these observations may not be unrelated at the cellular level.

The effect of these compounds as growth inhibitors in plants and
the mitotic effects on plant cells extends the area of applied biochemistry to a very wide field for these compounds.  Indeed, with
the current methods of synthesis available and the accumulated
knowledge concerning the factors that affect the observed phenom-
ena, additional studies in any area concerned with these compounds
should be rewarding.

New knowledge is desperately needed concerning the production
of this type of compound during food spoilage.  The very high toxicity observed and the frequent occurrence of coumarin compounds
associated with products created either as metabolites of mold
growth or as products created in the mold mycelia on certain food
materials demands further exploration.

The present review, pointing out the strong synergistic action
of the furocoumarins and ultraviolet light, has not simplified the
toxicologic solution to the problems in this area, but rather has
been organized to provide a challenge to those concerned with the
health and happiness of man.

References

Birmingham, D. J., M. M. Key, G. E. Tubich, and V. B. Perone,
    1961, Arch. Dermatol., 83, 73.

Bloomfield, M., 1897, Hymns of Atharra-Veda, Vol. XLII,
    Clarendon Press, Oxford, England.

Chakraborty, D. P., A. Das Gupta, and P. K. Bose, 1957,
    Annals Biochem. Exp. Med., 17, 57.

Curtis, A. C., 1959, J. Invest. Dermatol., 32, 133.

El-Mofty, A., A. M. El-Mofty, H. Abdelal, and M. F. S. El-
    Haworg, 1959, J. Invest. Dermatol., 32, 645, 651.

Fahmy, I. R., and H. Abu-Shady, 1947, Quart. J. Pharm.
    Pharmacol., 20, 281.

Fitzpatrick, T. B., and M. A. Pathak, 1959, J. Invest. Dermatol.,
    32, 229.

Fowlks, W. L., 1959, J. Invest. Dermatol., 32, 233.

Gupta, S. R., and T. R. Seshadri, 1953, Proc. Indian Acad.
Sci., Section A37, 681.

Hoekenga, M. T., 1959, J. Invest. Dermatol., 32, 351.

Hoernle, A. F. R., 1893-1912, Bower Manuscript, Gov't.
Printing, Calcutta, India.

Kaufman, K. D., 1961, J. Org. Chem., 26, 117.

Khadzhai, Y. I., and V. F. Kuznetsova, 1962, Farmatscot. Zh.,
17, 57.

Khadzhai, Y. I., and V. F. Kuznetsova, 1963, Farmakol. i
Toksikol., 26, 219.

Kuske, H., 1938, Arch. Dermatol. u. Syphilis, 178, 112.

Labby, D. H., J. D. Imbrie, and T. B. Fitzpatrick, 1959, J.
Invest. Dermatol., 32, 273.

Musajo, L., 1955, Farmaco (Pavia), Ed. Sci., 10, 2.

Pathak, M. A., B. Allen, D. J. E. Ingram, and J. H. Fellman,
1961, Biochim. Biophys. Acta, 54, 506.

Pathak, M. A., F. Daniels, and T. B. Fitzpatrick, 1962, J.
Invest. Dermatol., 39, 225.

Pathak, M. A., and J. H. Fellman, 1960, Proc. Intern. Congr.
Photobiol., 3rd, Copenhagen, p. 552.

Pathak, M. A., J. H. Fellman, and K. D. Kaufman, 1960, J.
Invest. Dermatol., 35, 165.

Pathak, M. A., and T. B. Fitzpatrick, 1959, J. Invest. Dermatol.
32, 509.

Perone, V. B., L. D. Scheel, and R. A. Meitus, 1964, J. Invest.,
Dermatol., 42, 267.

Rodighiero, G., 1954, Giorn. Biochim., 3, 138.

Scheel, L. D., V. B. Perone, R. L. Larkin, and R. E. Kugel,
1963, Biochem., 2, 1127.

Seshadri, T. R., and M. S. Sood, 1963, Indian J. Chem., 1(7),
291.

Spath, E., and H. Holzen, 1933, Chem. Bericht, 66, 1137.

Thomas, H., 1911, Chem. Bericht, 44, 3325.

Tucker, H. A., 1959, J. Invest. Dermatol., 32, 277.

Vorsatz, F., 1936, J. Prakt. Chem., 145, 265.

# AN ESTROGENIC METABOLITE PRODUCED BY FUSARIUM GRAMINEARUM IN STORED CORN

C. J. Mirocha, C. M. Christensen, and G. H. Nelson
Institute of Agriculture and College of Veterinary Medicine
University of Minnesota
St. Paul, Minnesota

The first report of an estrogenic condition in swine associated with consumption of fungus-infested feed was made by McNutt et al. (1928). He observed that sows which had consumed moldy feed developed enlarged, tense, and elevated vulvae, enlarged mammary glands, and, in more severe cases, a prolapse of the vagina and rectum. McErlean (1952) reported a similar condition of swine in Ireland in 1952 associated with the feeding of Fusarium-infested barley. Recently, Stob et al. (1962) isolated an anabolic and uterotrophic compound from corn infected with Fusarium that appeared to be responsible for the estrogenic syndrome.

Christensen et al. (1965) isolated an estrogenic metabolite produced by Fusarium, which they called F-2. It was found in autoclaved corn inoculated with Fusarium, in samples of corn feed from farms in Minnesota reporting the estrogenic symptoms in their swine herds, as well as in commercially prepared pelleted feed. When this material was injected into virgin white weanling female rats, it caused greatly enlarged uteri. When fed ad libitum to swine, it caused swollen, edematous vulvae in females, shrunken testes in young males, enlarged mammary glands in the young of both sexes, and abortion in pregnant gilts or sows. The estrogen F-2 is produced by certain isolates of the fungus Fusarium graminearum when grown on autoclaved moist corn.

To date, this estrogenic metabolite is important in explaining diseases in the field of veterinary medicine heretofore called idiopathic, although it may also have an unexplored significance in the area of public health as well as a potential use in medicine.

The early work on the chemical isolation and structure of the estrogenic metabolite was reported by Andrews and Stob (1961; 1965) and it was partially characterized by Christensen et al. (1965). Preliminary information on the chemical structure of the estrogen reveals it to be one of the enantiomorphs of 6-(10-

hydroxy-6-oxo-trans-1-undecenyl)-β-resorcylic acid lactone
called by the trivial name of zearalenone (Urry et al., 1966).

Compounds similar in structure to the estrogenic factor but
perhaps not in biological activity have been reported before.
These include curvularin produced by the fungi Curvularia sp.,
Penicillium steckii Zaleski, and P. expansum Link (Shibata et
al., 1964), and radicicol and monorden produced, respectively,
by Nectria radicicola (Mirrington et al., 1964) and Monosporium
sp. (McCapra et al., 1964). These last two appear to be identical. All are closely related to F-2 in structure, differing only
by the presence of an epoxy group, one extra carbonyl, and position of the conjugated double bonds.

## Materials and Methods

All solvents used in this study were of analytical reagent grade
except for petroleum ether (b.p. 30 to 60°C), which was of a
practical grade. Reagents (chlorotrimethylsilane and 1,1,1,3,3,
3-hexamethyldisilazane) used for the synthesis of the trimethylsilyl
ether of the estrogen (F-2) was purchased from Eastman Organic
Chemicals, and each was added individually to the substrate in anhydrous pyridine solution instead of adding a prepared mixture of
the reagents. Silica gel used as the adsorbent in column chromatography was of reagent grade, Fisher Certified, 100 to 200 mesh.
Ultraviolet absorption spectra were recorded with a Beckman DB
recording spectrophotometer. Analyses by elemental combustion,
mass spectrum, fluorescence emission, and infrared spectroscopy were carried out in the Chemistry Department of the University of Minnesota.

In experiments involving the effect of F-2 on the uterus of the
rat, the estrogen was administered by first dissolving it in pro-
pylene glycol and injecting it intramuscularly every second day
for 7 days. As far as possible, aseptic conditions were used in
the preparation and administration of the estrogen.

Studies involving the biosynthesis of F-2 were carried out by
seeding sterile, autoclaved corn with spores of Fusarium graminearum, incubating at room temperature (25 to 28°C) for 2 weeks,
and then transferring to a chamber held at 12°C for the duration
of the experiment. The fungus was stored on sterilized soil until
ready for seeding of the culture flasks. The fungus retains its
viability for months or years in such soil and undergoes no genetic
change.

The lability of the estrogenic compound when subjected to ultraviolet irradiation was determined by irradiating the compound in
a solution of ethanol with a General Electric blacklight lamp having
a peak of emission around 365 mμ and a fluorescent sun lamp emit-
ting at 312 mμ. The sample was kept in a sealed quartz cuvette
during the irradiation period, and the absorption spectrum was

monitored at appropriate time intervals. The total energy incident upon the sample illuminated with the General Electric blacklight lamp was $3.7 \times 10^3$ ergs/cm$^2$/sec. The fluorescent sun lamp was used in combination with a Corning CS-54 ultraviolet transmitting and visible light absorbing filter. The energy incident upon the sample was $1.5 \times 10^3$ ergs/cm$^2$/sec.

## Results and Discussion

Estrogenic response in rats. When the purified F-2 crystalline substance was injected into white weanling virgin female rats, a typical estrogenic response reflected in the increase in fresh weight of the uterus was found. A dosage response curve can be seen in Figure 1A, obtained when a cumulative dose ranging from 20 µg to 650 µg was administered over a period of 7 days. There was a linear response in the increase in the weight of the uterus corresponding to increase of F-2 concentration. The opposite was true, however, when the body weight of the animals was averaged. Those rats treated with the highest concentration of F-2 (Figure 1B) showed no increase in body weight when compared with the control rats, whereas the lowest concentrations

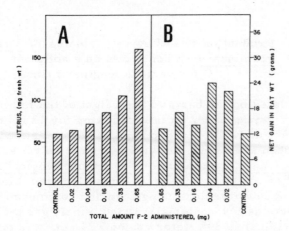

Fig. 1.  (A) Effect of different dosages of F-2 on the weight of the rat uterus when administered by intramuscular injection. (B) Effect of the same concentrations of F-2 on the body weight of the rat.

caused a relative increase in weight. This appears to be a typical hormonal, concentration-dependent response, which may suggest that caution should be taken if this compound were to be used as feed additive to promote growth in animals.

Biosynthesis of F-2 by Fusarium. Best production of the estrogen F-2 was obtained by growing the organism on moist, autoclaved corn for 2 weeks at 25 to 28°C followed by a temperature
of 12°C for different amounts of time.   Yields from two estrogen-
producing isolates of Fusarium graminearum designated as numbers 9 and 10 are shown in Figure 2.   As much as 3500 ppm of

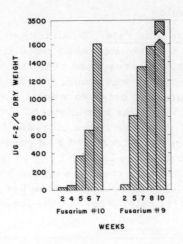

Fig. 2.   Production of F-2 by two isolates of Fusarium
graminearum when grown on a solid corn medium at 12°C for various lengths of time.

F-2, calculated on the basis of the weight of the finely ground substrate after drying under an infrared lamp for 12 hours, was found
after 8 weeks at 12°C.   Production of F-2 in a defined, liquid medium has been attempted, but yields are not as yet satisfactory.

Extraction and Quantitation of F-2 from Biological Material.
The following method of chemical extraction from biological material has been worked out using corn and commercial pelleted
feed products as test material.   Dried, finely ground biological
material, (adjust to 30% water content) 20 gm, was processed in
a Soxhlet extractor overnight, or for 16 hours, with 120 ml methylene chloride.   If a highly pigmented extract resulted, the methylene chloride was reextracted with acetonitrile in the following
manner: The methylene chloride was concentrated on a flash evaporator until the consistency was syruplike, but it was not allowed
to dry completely.   The concentrate was transferred into a sepa-
ratory funnel by rinsing with petroleum ether (b. p. 30 to 60°C).
Acetonitrile, 50 ml, was added; the mixture shaken; and the phases
allowed to separate.   The bottom phase (acetonitrile) should contain the F-2, and the top phase (petroleum ether) should contain
most of the pigments.   If the phases were inverted or an emulsion

formed, this usually could be corrected by adding a small amount
of the petroleum ether to the funnel.  The bottom layer was harvested, and the top phase reextracted with 25 ml acetonitrile in the
same manner.  The combined acetonitrile extracts (or the methylene chloride extract) were concentrated to about 3 ml, transferred to a small graduated vial, and brought up to 4 ml with chloroform or methylene chloride.  Analyses at this point were made
by the following methods.

  <u>Thin-layer chromatography</u>.  Thin-layer plates of silica gel
(E. Merck Ag.) were prepared in the conventional manner and
then activated at 100°C for 1 hour.  The extract (50 µl), a known
F-2 solution, a co-spot of F-2, and the unknown were applied.
The plates were developed in a solution of 5% ethanol in chloroform and checked for fluorescence at the same Rf value (0.5) as
the standard under illumination with an ultraviolet lamp.  An
authentic sample of F-2 emits light at 450 mµ when excited by a
wavelength of 310 mµ.

  <u>Ultraviolet spectrophotometry</u>.  After 5 µl of the extract was
placed in a cuvette in 2 ml of absolute ethanol, the wavelength
of the spectrophotometer was set at 276 mµ, and the sample was
diluted until the transmission registered between 30 and 50 per
cent.  The sample was then scanned between 340 and 200 mµ.  If
F-2 was present, maximum peaks of absorption were found at
314, 274, and 236 mµ.  The amount of F-2 present was computed
from a standard curve calculated at either one of the three wave-

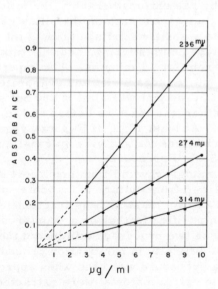

Fig. 3.  Straight-line relationships between different con-
         centrations of F-2 in ethanol when measured at
         236, 274, and 314 mµ.

lengths (Figure 3); best quantitative results were obtained using 274 mμ.

Gas-liquid chromatography. Advantage was taken of the fact that F-2 is a phenolic compound with two hydroxy groups that can be converted to their corresponding tri- or dimethylsilyl ethers and injected directly into the gas chromatograph.

The following equipment and conditions were used:

Aerograph HI-FY, Model 600C, Hydrogen flame; Column:
5 feet ss 1/8" packed with 5% SE-30 and 60/80 Chromosorb W.
Column temperature: 238°C
Injection block temperature: 280°C
Helium carrier gas-flow rate: 25 ml/min
Hydrogen flow rate: 25 ml/min
Honeywell Brown Recorder speed: Slow-2 (6.4 mm/min)

The trimethylsilyl ether derivatives of F-2 were prepared by adding 0.1 ml pyridine, 0.1 ml chlorotrimethylsilane, and 0.2 ml hexamethyldisilazane to 0.1 ml of the extract. Caution must be taken to add the reagents only in the order listed. The mixture was placed in 1-dram vials, stoppered tightly, and allowed to rest for 30 minutes before injecting. The retention time on the column was about 12 minutes at 238°C and 2.5 minutes at 261°C (Figure 4A). The limit of sensitivity of this method was 0.4 μg (Figure 4B).

To confirm the identification of F-2 present on a thin-layer chromatoplate by gas chromatography, the following procedure was used: The fluorescent area on the silica gel G chromatoplate was scraped into a small centrifuge tube, 2 ml of methylene-chloride were added with stirring, and this mixture was centri-fuged at 15,000 rpm for 15 minutes. The supernatant solution was poured off into a 1-dram vial and evaporated under nitrogen until the bottom of the vial was almost dry but still moist. The trimethylsilyl ether was made as before and injected into the gas chromatograph. At least 10 μg of F-2 was required on the plate to make the derivatives for analysis by gas-liquid chromatography.

Preparative Scale Procedures.

Column chromatography and countercurrent distribution. To obtain yields of F-2 from culture in amounts sufficient for crys-tallization, the extract must first be fractionated on a silica-gel column and then purified further on a countercurrent distribution apparatus. These two processes eliminated the pigments that create the most difficulty in purification procedures.

The following procedure was used when approximately 400 to 500 grams of biological material were extracted. The sample was extracted as already described using the acetonitrile clean-up procedure. The acetonitrile was concentrated to a syruplike consistency in a flash evaporator and the precipitate brought into solution with a minimum amount of chloroform. A column of sil-

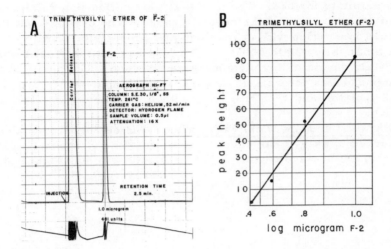

Fig. 4.  (A) Separation of the trimethylsilyl ether of F-2 by
gas-liquid chromatography.  (B) Straight-line relationship between the peak height of the trimethylsilyl ether of F-2 and concentration between 0.4
and 1.0 μg when separated by gas-liquid chromatography.

ica gel (Fisher Certified, 100 to 200 mesh) 2 × 25 cm was prepared by slurring the activated silica gel into the column with chloroform.  The column was loaded with the extract by using chloroform and then eluted with 500 ml of petroleum ether (b. p. 30 to
60°C) and approximately 3000 ml of methylene chloride.  The methylene chloride effluent was collected in 100 ml fractions and monitored for the presence of F-2 in each container with the spectrophotometer.  The best F-2 preparation was combined, concentrated,
and saved for countercurrent distribution.

The effluent containing the F-2 was concentrated to a convenient
volume (10 to 25 ml) for use on a 200-tube countercurrent distribution apparatus where each transfer tube holds 10 ml of the
top and 10 ml of the bottom phase.  The phase system that proved
to be most efficient was made up of petroleum ether (b. p. 30 to
60°C), water, methanol, diethyl ether (2:1:3:5).  In this solvent
system, F-2 had a partition ratio (K) of 1.2.  The equilibration
time of this system is 1.5 minutes, and the F-2 was found in tubes
50 through 76, with the best preparation in tubes 62 and 63.  These
were combined and saved for crystallization.

Crystallization.  The combined fractions obtained from the countercurrent distribution apparatus were concentrated and enough
chloroform added so that all the material was in solution.  Petro-

leum ether (b. p. 60 to 70°C) was then added drop by drop until
a precipitate formed.  The material was chilled in a refrigerator,
then centrifuged, and the crystals saved.  The crystals were again
placed in solution with chloroform and reprecipitated with petroleum ether (b. p. 30 to 60°C).  The cycle was repeated until white
crystals devoid of any pigment were obtained.  The purity of the
compound was determined by separating on thin-layer chromatography plates and then charring with a methanolic solution of
$H_2SO_4$.

Physical and Chemical Properties.  The estrogenic metabolite
referred to as F-2 has characteristic maxima of absorption in the
ultraviolet at wavelengths of 314, 274, and 236 mμ (Figure 5).

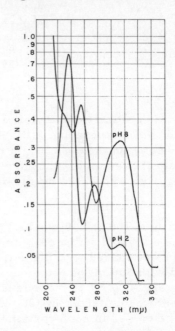

WAVELENGTH (mμ)

Fig. 5.   Absorbance of F-2 in the ultraviolet when measured
         at pH 2 in ethanol.  Upon addition of base, a batho-
         chromic shift to the higher wavelength results, as
         can be seen by the curve labeled pH 8.

Its melting point lies between 163 and 165°C.  We have determined
the molecular weight as 318 by both elemental and mass spectrometer analyses.  Mass spectrometer analyses were made immediately after separation by gas-liquid chromatography and by conventional means with identical results.  The proposed structure
of the compound as reported by Andrews and Stob (1961; 1965) and
Urry et al. (1966) is shown in Figure 6.

Compound F-2 fluoresces blue-green when excited by ultraviolet radiation.  An emission spectrum can be seen in Figure 7, ob-

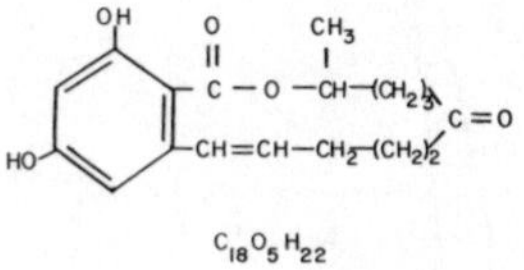

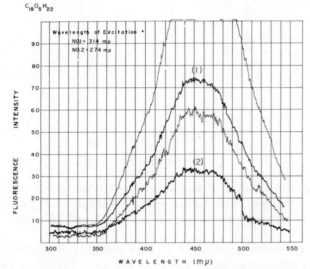

Fig. 6.   Structural formula of the
estrogenic factor F-2.

Fig. 7.   Fluorescence emission spectrum of F-2 in
ethanol when irradiated at wavelengths of
314 mμ and 274 mμ.

tained after irradiation at 314 and 274 mμ.  As expected, the intensity of fluorescence was greater when excited with radiation
at the higher wavelength.   The fluorescence at 450 mμ is useful
for the detection of the compound on thin-layer chromatoplates.

When treated with base in ethanolic solution, F-2 exhibits a
characteristic bathochromic shift toward the higher wavelength.
The band at 236 mμ shifts to 256 mμ, the weak band at 314 mμ becomes broad and strong, and the band of absorption at 276 mμ disappears (Figure 5).   This bathochromic shift is reversed immedi-
atly upon acidification.

The estrogen gave a positive response for a phenol with $FeCl_3$,
and the keto group reacted with 2,4 dinitrophenylhydrazine to form
the corresponding hydrazone.

When the purified compound as separated on a thin-layer chromatoplate was sprayed with 50% $H_2SO_4$ in methanol, it immediately
turned light green and then quickly turned yellow; after charring
at 100°C for 10 minutes, it turned a yellowish brown.

Results involving the lability of F-2 when irradiated with ultraviolet radiation can be seen in Figure 8.   The ordinate represents

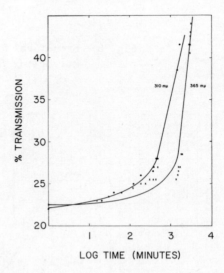

Fig. 8. Sensitivity of F-2 in ethanol when subjected to continuous irradiation with ultraviolet lamps that emit
strongly at wavelengths of 310 and 365 mμ.

the per cent transmission of F-2 as monitored at 274 mμ although
the entire spectrum was examined for any change at each time of
sampling. Similar curves were obtained when irradiated at 312 mμ
and 365 mμ although F-2 broke down more quickly at the lower
wavelength. The greatest change in its absorption spectrum took
place between 8 and 24 hours when irradiated at 310 mμ and between 31 and 47 hours when irradiated at 365 mμ. It is therefore
concluded that the estrogen is relatively stable to ultraviolet irradiation when contained in ethanol. It would appear that this region of the spectrum does not afford a good means of degradation
of F-2.

Heat stability of the F-2. Tests were conducted in both absolute and 50% ethanol to determine the stability of the estrogenic
factor. The absorption maximum at 276 mμ was monitored to
determine if any change had occurred over the period of heating.

When heated in absolute ethanol for 30 minutes at 60°C, no
change occurred. When heated in 50% water-ethanol solution for
30 minutes at 60°C, no change occurred, but at 111°C there was
a slow decomposition. Care was taken to note that the change in
the absorption spectrum, not change in biological activity, was
used as the criterion of evaluation.

Infrared analyses. Analyses of the infrared absorption spectrum
of F-2 were made in chloroform, Nujol mull, and KBr pellet. Best
results were obtained by using the latter, which is shown in Figure 9. The strongest absorption maxima were found at the following frequencies expressed as cm$^{-1}$: 3300; 2925; 1688; 1645; 1612;
1578; 1460; 1435; 1380; 1350; 1312; 1254; 1194; 1166; 1102; 1070;

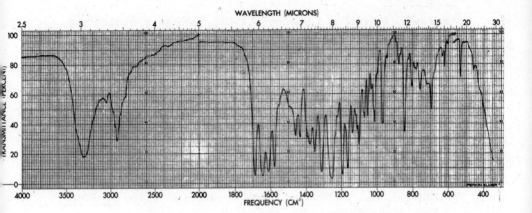

Fig. 9.   Infrared absorption spectrum of a KBr pellet
preparation of F-2.

1053; 1013; 968; 845; 760; 697. The greatest attention in the
infrared study was paid to the presence or absence of the ketone
and lactone function. The strong absorption at 1688 cm$^{-1}$ suggested a ketone or the lactone function. To distinguish between
the two, the keto group was reduced mildly with sodium borohy-
dride, and the resulting derivative was anlyzed by infrared. The
strong absorption band at 1688 cm$^{-1}$ disappeared, whereas the
band at 1645 cm$^{-1}$ remained. It is assumed that the latter absorption maximum represents the lactone function. Reduction of the
ketone did not change the ultraviolet absorption spectrum.

The estrogenic factor described here appeared to be identical
to the compound described by Andrews and Stob (1961; 1965) and
Urry et al. (1966). It has been called by various trivial names
in the literature such as "F-2" by the Minnesota group (Christensen et al., 1965), "RAL" by Commercial Solvents Corporation,
and more recently as "Zearalenone" (Urry et al., 1966).

We have isolated this compound from samples of feed submitted
to our laboratory and suspected to be involved in inciting the estrogenic syndrome in swine. We are now concerned with the possible presence of this compound in maize products used for human
consumption. Because of the similarity between the hog's re-
productive system and physiology and the human, we are very
much concerned with the possible significance of this estrogen in
medicine.

Studies are currently in progress concerning the biosynthesis
of F-2 by fusarium on various media as well as the metabolic pathway of its production by the fungus.

References

Andrews, F. N., and M. Stob, 1961, Substance Anabolique, Belgian Patent 611630.

Andrews, F. N., and M. Stob, 1965, Anabolic and estrogenic compound and process of making, U.S. Patent 3,196,019.

Christensen, C. M., G. H. Nelson, and C. J. Mirocha, 1965, Appl. Microbiol., 13, 653.

McCapra, F., A. I. Scott, P. Delmotte, J. Delmotte-Plaquee, and N. S. Bhacca, 1964, Tetrahedron Letters, 15, 869.

McErlean, B. A., 1952, Vet. Rec., 64, 539.

McNutt, S. H., P. Purwin, and C. Murray, 1928, J. Amer. Vet. Med. Assoc., 73, 484.

Mirrington, B. N., E. Ritchie, C. W. Shoppee, W. C. Taylor, and S. Sternhell, 1964, Tetrahedron Letters, 7, 365.

Shibata, S., S. Natori, and S. Udagana, 1964, List of Fungal Products, University of Tokyo Press, Japan.

Stob, M., R. S. Baldwin, J. Tuite, F. N. Andrews, and K. G. Gillette, 1962, Nature, 196(4861), 1318.

Urry, W. H., H. L. Wehrmeister, E. B. Hodge, and P. H. Hidy, 1966, Tetrahedron Letters, 27, 3109.

# PRODUCTION OF FLUORESCENT COMPOUNDS OTHER THAN AFLATOXINS BY JAPANESE INDUSTRIAL MOLDS

Tamotsu Yokotsuka, Masaoki Sasaki, Tadaaki Kikuchi,
Yasuo Asao, Akio Nobuhara
Noda Institute for Scientific Research
and
Central Research Institute of Kikkoman Shoyu Co. Ltd.,
Noda, Japan

## Introduction

Extensive investigations for toxin-producing microbes that con-taminate foodstuffs are currently being conducted. In Japan, molds belonging to Aspergillus soyae or oryzae groups have been utilized for centuries as enzymatic sources for the production of such foods as shoyu (fermented liquid of soybeans and wheat), miso (fermented paste of soybeans, barley, and/or rice), sake (fermented rice wine), amasake (saccharified rice), and mirin (saccharified rice with high concentration of alcohol). Similar types of foods are found in the other Oriental countries such as Taiwan, China, and Korea, among others. The ability of some strains of Aspergillus flavus to pro-duce aflatoxins (Nesbitt et al., 1962; Asao et al., 1963; Chang et al., 1963) and other toxic substances (C. W. Hesseltine, J. J. Ellis, O. L. Shotwell, and R. D. Stubbelfield, 1965, private com-munication) stimulated us to conduct intensive investigations into the toxin-producing capabilities of these Oriental industrial molds. This is a report of our findings.

Some investigators have reported negative data (C. W. Hesseltine, J. J. Ellis, O. L. Shotwell, and R. D. Stubbelfield, 1965, private communication; Aibara and Miyaki, 1965; Masuda et al., 1965) concerning aflatoxin production by Japanese industrial molds and its occurrence in fermented products. However, the methods ap-plied and the basis for conclusions in these studies seem to have been limited to comparisons of $R_f$ values on thin-layer chromato-grams and the fluorescence spectra of the spots. In the present work, 73 industrial strains of Aspergillus mold that were used ei-ther for production or found in food preparations were examined first for their production of fluorescent compounds after culture in zinc containing Czapek Dox medium (Nesbitt et al., 1962). To our

131

surprise, about 30% of these strains, including molds used for
preparations manufactured by the major Japanese food industries,
produced compounds that are very similar to those of aflatoxins
in fluorescence spectra and $R_f$ values on thin-layer chromatograms.
Further chemical examination of the eluates of these spots demonstrated, however, that these compounds were not aflatoxins. Instead, a number of substances resembling flavacol (Dunn et al.,
1949) and aspergillic acid and condensation products of two molecules of amino acids (such as leucine and isoleucine) were identified.

Solvent extracts of these spots were intraperitoneally injected
into mice, and the results indicate that there were no substances
more toxic than aspergillic acid. Attention was then focused on
aspergillic acid although it is not carcinogenic and its toxicity is
not particularly great. It should be noted that the wild strain X-1
(Table 1) gave the greatest production of aspergillic acid in Czapek
Dox or modified Meyer medium. However, this strain did not
produce aspergillic acid when cultured on raw materials used in
preparation of the foods just mentioned, namely, mixture of soybeans and wheat or rice by the culture methods conventionally employed in these industries. This seems to be due in part to the very
short time of cultivation employed in industries. Accordingly, we
could not detect the presence of aspergillic acid in these foods. It
should be noted that solvent extracts of the finished food products
were not toxic for mice when administered at dosages corresponding to the equivalent of consumption by a man for several months.
In considering such toxicologic experiments, the content of salt,
alcohol, fusel oils, food additives, and the total amount consumed
must also be taken into account. These toxicological data will be
discussed in a separate communication, and only the isolation and
identification of organic compounds are described in the present
report.

The molds that are commonly used in Japanese food industries
are classified as Aspergillus soyae or oryzae. Sakaguchi and
Yamada (1944) once pointed out that the Aspergillus flavus-oryzae
group of Thom and Church (1926) includes many species, but does
not include some strains of Aspergillus used for food preparations in Japan. Recently, Murakami et al. (1966) considered that
A. flavus ATCC 15517, which produces aflatoxins, is correctly
classified as A. parasiticus. In Japan, A. flavus, A. soyae, A.
oryzae, and A. parasiticus are clearly differentiated and are believed to be quite different species.

Concerning fluorescent compounds produced by Japanese Aspergillus molds, Kihara et al. (1948) identified bluish-violet and
bluish-white fluorescent compounds differing from flavin. Recently, Kaneko (1965, 1966) has reported production of isoxanthop-
terin, $C_{13}H_{17}O_7N_5(H_2O)$ mp 193°C, a compound exhibiting green fluorescence by A. oryzae. We (Asao and Yokotsuka, 1958) reported

production of ferulic acid by a shoyu mold. Its fluorescence is
bluish-violet, and the same compound was identified in Japanese
rice wine by Takase et al. (1965). In the present work, ergosterol and its degradation compounds with bluish-violet fluorescence
as well as degradation products of kojic acid with green fluorescence were isolated from mycelium and broth of A. oryzae. These
compounds differ from aflatoxins with respect to their $R_f$ values
on chromatograms.

## Materials and Methods

Mold Strains Tested. The 73 strains (Table 1) were tested, 45
from seed molds or starters on the market and 28 from our stock
cultures, which included about 10 from prominent companies. Of
the 73, 27 are used for production of shoyu, 16 for miso, 28 chiefly
for alcoholic beverages, and 2 are wild strains. Almost all be-
long to the Aspergillus soyae or oryzae group, but the strains for

aflatoxin B1
$C_{17}H_{12}O_6$

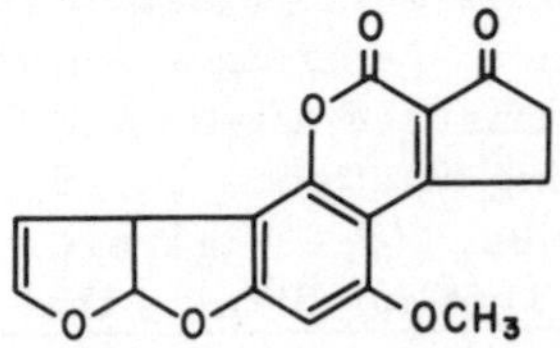

aflatoxin B2
$C_{17}H_{14}O_6$

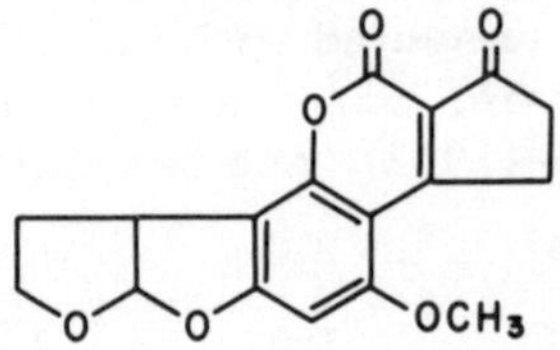

aflatoxin G1
$C_{17}H_{12}O_7$

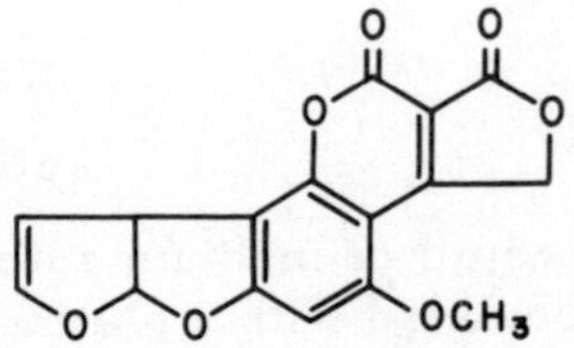

aflatoxin G2
$C_{17}H_{14}O_7$

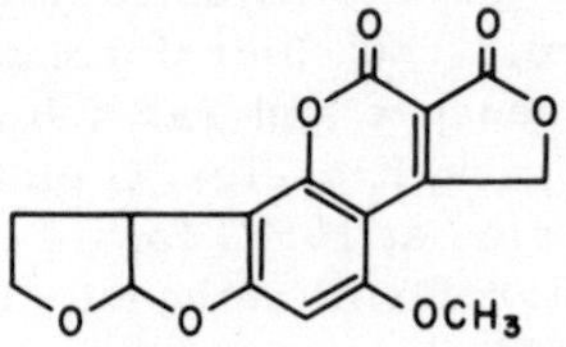

Fig. 1. Structures of the known aflatoxins.

alcoholic beverages also include the so-called "black molds," A. niger and A. usami, among others. Strain X-1 and X-3 are not industrial strains but are wild strains that were isolated because of their superior production of aflatoxinlike fluorescent compounds. They were stored on agar slants containing koji extract.

Preparation of Authentic Aflatoxins. Two kg of crushed wheat, moistened with 2 kg of water and autoclaved at 15 lbs pressure for 20 minutes, were inoculated with A. flavus ATCC 15517 and incubated at 30°C for 14 days in a flat flask. The final culture was extracted with an equal amount of chloroform and the extraction repeated three times. The chloroform was evaporated at 55°C under reduced pressure, and the concentrate was mixed with 20 volumes of petroleum ether. The resulting precipitate was separated and dissolved in a small amount of chloroform. This solution was submitted to thin-layer chromatography in accordance with conventional methods (Chang et al., 1963; G. N. Wogan, 1964, private communication). Compounds eluted from the chromatograms were recrystallized and were checked by ultraviolet (UV) absorption spectrum and infrared (IR) spectrum (Hartley et al., 1963). Purified aflatoxins $B_1$ and $G_1$ as well as the precipitate containing aflatoxins $B_1$, $B_2$, $G_1$, and $G_2$ were used as authentic samples. (See Figure 1 for structures.)

Screening Test for Strains that Produce Aflatoxinlike Substances. The screening test was essentially that described by Nesbitt et al. (1962) and Wogan (1964, private communication). Czapek Dox medium supplemented with zinc, believed to be the best for detecting aflatoxin, was prepared in accordance with the method of Nesbitt et al. (1962), and has the following composition:

| | | | | |
|-----------|--------|--------|--------|----|
| $NaNO_3$ | 2.0 g | $FeSO_4$ | 0.01 g | |
| $K_2HPO_4$ | 1.0 | $ZnSO_4$ | 0.2 | |
| $MgSO_4$ | 0.5 | Sucrose | 30.0 | |
| KCl | 0.5 | Water | 1000.0 | ml |
| | | pH | 6 - 7 | |

Two hundred ml of medium autoclaved in a 1-liter Fernbach flask was inoculated with 3 platinum loopfuls of organisms from agar slants and still cultured for 9 days at 30°C. The broth filtered through gauze was extracted three times with 1/3 volume of chloroform. The chloroform solution was concentrated at 55°C at reduced pressure and was submitted to thin-layer chromatography analysis on Kieselgel G plates, 0.25 mm in thickness, activated by drying at 105°C for 12 hours. The plates were developed with chloroform:methanol 98:2 (v/v). Strains that produced compounds with fluorescence and $R_f$ values resembling those of aflatoxins in ultraviolet light of 365 mμ were studied further.

Separation of Aflatoxin B-Like Compounds from Cultures of Test Strains. Aspergillus strain HR5-1 and the wild strain X-1 were mainly employed for these experiments.  The methods were almost the same as those employed in the screening procedure, except that the volume of the culturing flask was changed from 1 liter to 5 liters with a corresponding increase in the amount of medium.  The cultivation period was prolonged to 15 to 20 days because higher yields were obtained by the longer cultivation.  Details of the fermentation and extraction procedures are shown in Figures 2 and 3.  Five blue-fluorescent, aflatoxinlike spots were

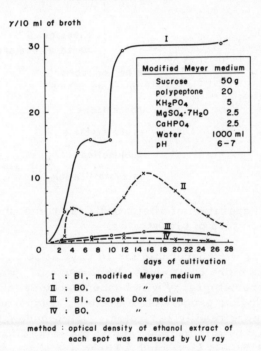

Fig. 2.  Formation of compounds B0 and B1 in culture of Aspergillus X-1.

designated B0, B1, B2, B3, and B4 in order of decreasing $R_f$ values.  Solvent extracts of each spot were submitted for determination of chemical structures.  Upon recognizing that these compounds were condensation products from amino acids, the culture medium was changed to the following composition:

| Sucrose | 50 | g | CaHPO$_4$ | 2.5 g |
|---|---|---|---|---|
| KH$_2$PO$_4$ | 5 | | Water | 1000.0 ml |
| MgSO$_4$7H$_2$O | 2.5 | | pH | 6 - 7 |
| Polypeptone | 20 | | | |

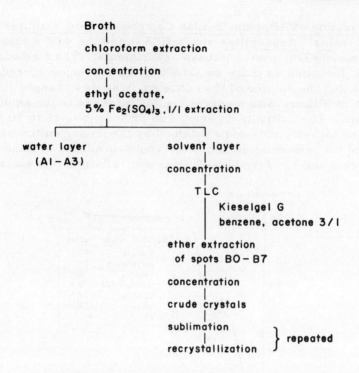

Fig. 3. Separation of aflatoxin B-like compounds from
culture of test strains.

The cultures were incubated for 10 days at 30°C. From this
culture, three more compounds, B5 through B7, were found by
thin-layer chromatography with benzene:acetone (60 to 65:40 to
35). With a higher proportion of acetone, compounds of the B
group were more readily separated. Compounds B5 through B7
were prepared by this method, and at the same time the yields
of compounds B0-B4 increased. These are shown in Figure 2
and, later, Figure 8, p. 143.

Separation of Nonfluorescent Compounds that Chelate with Iron.
When the above chromatograms were sprayed with 5% ferrous
sulfate, three brown spots appeared between B2 and the base line.
These are referred to as A1, A2, and A3. To separate these compounds, the chloroform extract of broth was directly submitted to
thin-layer chromatography analysis on 0.5 mm Kieselgel G plates.
Dark spots that absorbed ultraviolet light were scraped off and
eluted with ether. (See Figure 4.)

Separation of Compounds that Remained at the Origin on Thin-
Layer Chromatography Plates. The chloroform extract of the
spot on the base line was divided into three fractions, C1, C2,
and C3 as follows:

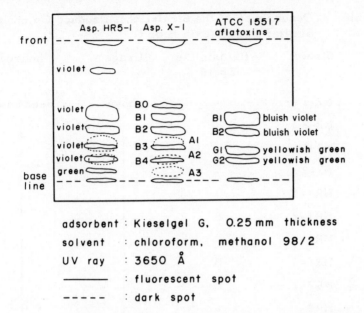

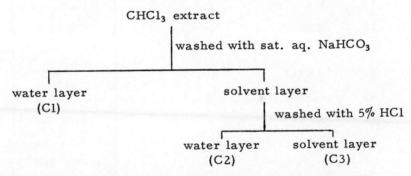

Fig. 4.    Typical TLC of aflatoxin B-like compounds of
Aspergillus X-1 and HR5-1, compared with
aflatoxins of Aspergillus flavus ATCC 15517.

### Separation of Fluorescent Compounds Contained in Mycelium.

Test strain HR5-1 was cultured for 15 to 20 days at 30°C in essentially the same manner as already described; 296 g of dry
mycelium from 80 liters of culture were extracted with water,
then with chloroform:methanol 3:1.    Upon concentration, a precipitate formed, which was washed with petroleum ether.    The
yield was 230 mg.

### Results

Occurrence of the Strains that Produce Blue-Violet or Yellow-
Green Fluorescent Compounds Resembling Aflatoxin $B_1$ or $G_1$.    The
results of this screening are shown in Table 1.    Compounds that

Table 1.  Occurrence of the Strains that Produce Compounds
          Similar to Aflatoxin B or G.

| No. | Strain | Aflatoxinlike Spots | Usage | Source |
|-----|--------|---------------------|-------|--------|
| 1 | N2-1 | - | Shoyu | Seed mold |
| 2 | N2-2 | - | | |
| 3 | N3-1 | - | | |
| 4 | N3-2 | - | | |
| 5 | HR1-1 | - | | |
| 6 | HR1-2 | B | | |
| 7 | HR2-1 | - | | |
| 8 | HR2-2 | B | | |
| 9 | HR2-3 | B | | |
| 10 | HR3 | - | | |
| 11 | M1-1 | - | | |
| 12 | M2-1 | G | | |
| 13 | M4-1 | G | | |
| 14 | KK2 | B | | |
| 15 | AK-1 | - | | |
| 16 | AK2-1 | G | | |
| 17 | AK2-2 | B | | |
| 18 | AK3 | - | | |
| 19 | KS-1 | G | | Stock culture of our research |
| 20 | 1046 | - | | |
| 21 | 1745 | - | | |
| 22 | 1-20 | - | | |
| 23 | 1-21 | - | | |
| 24 | 1-22 | B | | |
| 25 | 1-23 | B | | |
| 26 | 1-24 | B | | |
| 27 | 1-25 | B | | |
| 28 | X-1 | B | | Wild strain |

| No. | Strain | Aflatoxinlike Spots | Usage | Source |
|-----|--------|---------------------|-------|--------|
| 29 | X-3 | B | Shoyu | Wild strain |
| 30 | N-4 | - | Miso | Seed mold |
| 31 | N-5 | - | | |
| 32 | N-6 | G | | |
| 33 | N-7 | G | | |
| 34 | HR5-1 | B | | |
| 35 | HR5-2 | - | | |
| 36 | HR6-1 | - | | |
| 37 | HR6-2 | - | | |
| 38 | HR7-1 | - | | |
| 39 | HR7-2 | B | | |
| 40 | HR-8 | - | | |
| 41 | HR9-1 | - | | |
| 42 | HR9-2 | - | | |
| 43 | HR11 | - | | |
| 44 | KK-3 | - | | |
| 45 | KS-2 | G | | |
| 46 | HR4-1 | - | Alcoholic beverage | |
| 47 | HR4-2 | B | | |
| 48 | 1-28 | - | | |
| 49 | 1-29 | - | | |
| 50 | 1-30 | - | | |
| 51 | 1-31 | - | | |
| 52 | 1-32 | - | | |
| 53 | 1-33 | - | | |
| 54 | 1-34 | - | | |
| 55 | 1-35 | - | | |
| 56 | 1-36 | - | | |
| 57 | 1492 | - | | Stock culture of our research |

| No. | Strain | Aflatoxinlike Spots | Usage | Source |
|-----|--------|---------------------|-------|--------|
| 58 | 1527 | - | Alcoholic beverage | Stock culture of our research |
| 59 | 1528 | - | | |
| 60 | 1532 | - | | |
| 61 | 1597 | - | | |
| 62 | 1612 | - | | |
| 63 | 1627 | - | | |
| 64 | 1640 | - | | |
| 65 | 1672 | - | | |
| 66 | 1742 | - | | |
| 67 | 1783 | - | | |
| 68 | 1784 | G | | |
| 69 | 1785 | - | | |
| 70 | 1-26 | G | | |
| 71 | 1-27 | - | | |
| 72 | 4-1 | - | | |
| 73 | 4-2 | - | | |

resembled aflatoxin $B_1$ were produced by 14 strains, and 8 strains produced aflatoxin G-like spots. (See Figure 5.) Of the 14 strains, 5 fell in pattern II of Figure 6 and typically showed $R_f$ values and blue-violet fluorescence similar to those of aflatoxin $B_1$. A. Soyae X-1, which is a wild type, was the best producer, and HR5-1 was the second among them. Of the 8 strains, 4 fell in pattern II of Figure 7 and typically produced compounds similar to aflatoxin $G_1$ insofar as $R_f$ values and yellowish-green fluorescence were concerned. Aspergillus M4-1 was still another strain giving high yields of such compounds.

Comparison of Aflatoxinlike Compounds Produced by Various Molds Showing Authentic Aflatoxins by Ultraviolet Absorption Spectrum. Each compound B1 produced by 14 strains in Table 1, mostly resembling aflatoxin $B_1$ with respect to $R_f$ value, was eluted from thin-layer chromatography plates with ethanol, and their ultraviolet absorption spectra were examined. There were three similar patterns, shown in Figure 6, with common and strongest absorption at 310 to 330 mμ, while that of aflatoxin $B_1$ is 360 mμ (Hartley et al., 1963). Figure 7 shows that aflatoxin

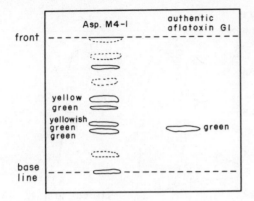

adsorbent : Kieselgel G,  0.25 mm thickness

solvent　　 : chloroform,  methanol 9/1

UV ray　　 : 3650 Å

————————— : fluorescent spot

— — — — — : weak fluorescent spot

Fig. 5.   Typical TLC of yellowish-green fluorescent compounds of <u>Aspergillus</u> M4-1, compared with authentic aflatoxin G1.

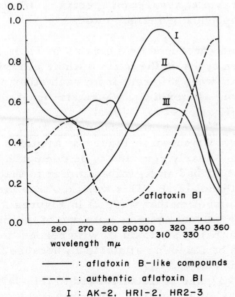

I : AK-2, HRI-2, HR2-3

II : X-I, X-3, HR5-I, I-24, I-25

III : HR2-2, I-23

Fig. 6.   Ultraviolet absorption spectra of aflatoxin B-like
compounds of various molds.

142                                        T. Yokotsuka et al.

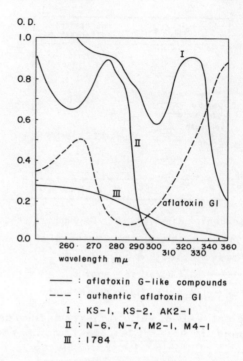

Fig. 7.   Ultraviolet absorption spectra of aflatoxin G-like
          compounds of various molds.

$G_1$-like compounds produced by 8 strains in Table 1 are also di-
visible into three types on the basis of their ultraviolet absorption spectra.  All were different from each other and they all
also differed from aflatoxin $G_1$, whose strongest absorption is
also at 360 mµ (Hartley et al., 1963).

Variation of $R_f$ Values of Compounds B0 to B7 with Different
Solvent Systems.  As shown in Figure 8, aflatoxin B-like compounds have been clearly revealed to be compounds other than
aflatoxins.  Spot B1 had an $R_f$ value similar to that of aflatoxin
$B_1$ in benzene:ethanol (9:1).  This was also true for the solvent
system of chloroform:methanol (98:2) in Figures 2 and 3.  Depending upon the solvent system, only one of the B0 to B7 spots
corresponded to that of aflatoxin $B_1$ with respect to $R_f$ values.
The same would be found for aflatoxin $B_2$ because its $R_f$ value is
between aflatoxins $B_1$ and $G_1$.

Each spot B0-B7 was again submitted to thin-layer chromatography solvent systems, but they uniformly had $R_f$ values different from those of aflatoxins.  These data also substantiate the
fact that B0 to B7 spots are different from aflatoxins $B_1$ and $B_2$
and indicate that these compounds are not aflatoxins.

Comparison of Ultraviolet Absorption Spectra of Compounds
B0 to B7.  Figure 9 shows that these 8 compounds have chemical

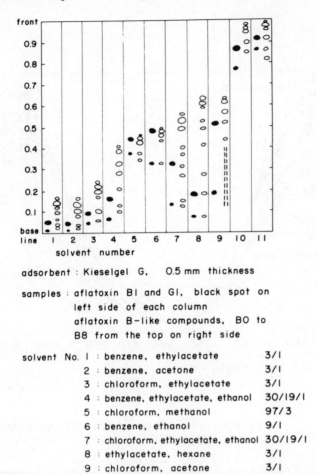

adsorbent : Kieselgel G,    0.5 mm thickness

samples : aflatoxin Bl and Gl, black spot on
left side of each column
aflatoxin B-like compounds, BO to
B8 from the top on right side

| solvent No. | | | |
|---|---|---|---|
| 1 | benzene, ethylacetate | 3/1 |
| 2 | benzene, acetone | 3/1 |
| 3 | chloroform, ethylacetate | 3/1 |
| 4 | benzene, ethylacetate, ethanol | 30/19/1 |
| 5 | chloroform, methanol | 97/3 |
| 6 | benzene, ethanol | 9/1 |
| 7 | chloroform, ethylacetate, ethanol | 30/19/1 |
| 8 | ethylacetate, hexane | 3/1 |
| 9 | chloroform, acetone | 3/1 |
| 10 | ethylacetate, methanol | 3/1 |
| 11 | acetone, hexane | 3/1 |

Fig. 8.  Variation of Rf values of aflatoxin B-like compounds
of Aspergillus X-1 with different solvent system.

structures that are very similar to those of aspergillic acid and
hydroxyaspergillic acid but are absolutely different from those of
aflatoxins.

Comparison of Infrared Spectra of Compounds B0 to B7.  Figures 10, 11, and 12 show that these 8 compounds are different
from aflatoxins.  Their chemical structures are similar to those
of aspergillic acid and hydroxyaspergillic acid with common absorption at 1600 to 1700 $cm^{-1}$, and different from these 2 compounds with strong absorption at 950 $cm^{-1}$.  The infrared spectra
of compounds B0, B2, B4, and B6 corresponded with those of
authentic 2-hydroxy-3:6-di-sec-butylpyrazine, flavacol, deoxyhydroxyaspergillic acid (Dutcher, 1957), and deoxyhydroxymuta-

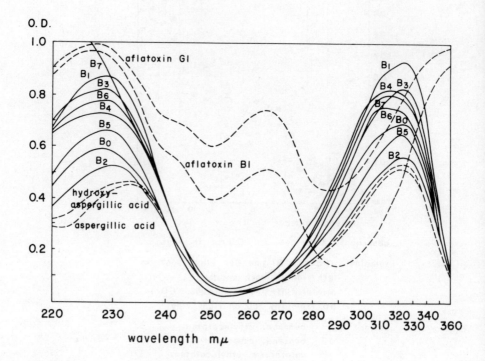

Fig. 9.    Ultraviolet absorption spectra of compounds
B0-B7 in ethanol.

aspergillic acid,* respectively.    Infrared spectra of compounds
B3, B5, and B7 are different from the other 5 compounds with
common absorption at about 3400 cm$^{-1}$.

The fluorescence spectra of compounds B0 to B4 are shown in
Figure 13.    These compounds have similar fluorescence properties, but different from those of the aflatoxins.    Some physical
and chemical properties and the structures of compounds B0-B7
are summarized in Tables 2 and 3.

Characterization of Compound A1 Produced by Aspergillus X-1.
Ether extracts containing the A1 fraction were recrystallized from
acetone and benzene and colorless hexagonal plates were obtained.
This compound was shown to be the zinc salt of aspergillic acid
by elementary analysis and infrared spectrum (Figure 10).

---

*Kindly supplied by Dr. S. Nakamura.    (See Nakamura and
Shiro, 1959.)

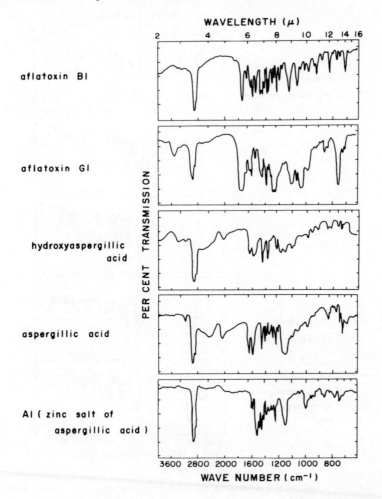

Fig. 10.   Infrared spectra of aflatoxin B1, G1, hydroxy-
           aspergillic acid, aspergillic acid, and com-
           pound A1.

$C_{24}H_{38}N_4Zn$            mp 230°C

|            | C    | H   | N    | Zn   |
|------------|------|-----|------|------|
| Analytic   | 56.2 | 7.2 | 10.9 | 11.9 |
| Calculated | 56.3 | 7.4 | 10.9 | 12.7 |

This compound decomposes into aspergillic acid by 5% sulfuric
acid, as confirmed by infrared spectroscopy.

Studies on the Precipitate Obtained from Mycelium of Aspergillus HR5-1.   The precipitate obtained as described previously
was purified by thin-layer chromatography with the solvent system chloroform-methanol (98:2).   A spot of $R_f$ 0.8, which showed

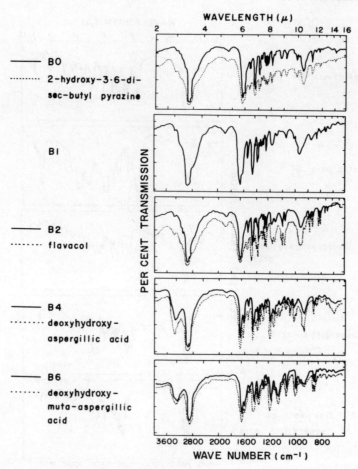

Fig. 11.   Infrared spectra of compounds B0, B1, B2, B4,
            and B6.

violet fluorescence in 365 mμ ultraviolet light, was eluted with
ether and recrystallized from hot benzene.  Colorless needles
with mp 131°C (decomposible and sublimatic) were obtained.  Elemental analysis, a strong absorption peak at 323 mμ in ultraviolet
light, absorption at 1650 cm⁻¹ in the infrared spectrum, and other
properties showed the compound to be ergosterol.  After leaving
these crystals in the air, they changed to other compounds of strong
green fluorescence with $R_f$ value a little higher than that of ergosterol.

Isolation and Identification of Kojic Acid.  A chloroform extract
of the broth cultured with HR5-1 was concentrated until a precipitate was formed.  The sublimed fraction of this was recrystallized
from ethanol and crystals of mp 151°C were obtained. The infrared
spectrum of this compound agreed with that of kojic acid. This purified kojic acid itself gave no fluorescence but upon standing in air

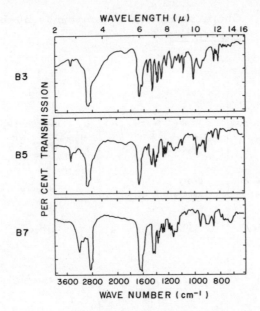

Fig. 12.  Infrared spectra of compounds B3, B5, and B7.

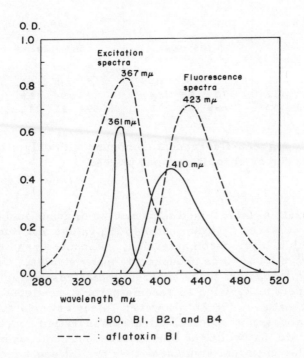

Fig. 13.  Excitation and fluorescence spectra of B0-B4
          compounds.

Table 2.   Characterization of compounds B0-B3 of Aspergillus X-1.

| Sample | B0 | B1 | B2 | B3 |
|---|---|---|---|---|
| Assigned chemical structure | (structure) | (structure) | (structure) | |
| Name of compound | 2-hydroxy-3·6-di-sec-butyl pyrazine | deoxy-aspergillic acid ? | flavacol | — |
| Molecular formula | $C_{12}H_{20}ON_2$ | $C_{12}H_{20}ON_2$ | $C_{12}H_{20}ON_2$ | — |
| Yield, mg/L Czapek Dox medium | 67 / 260 | 225 / 140 | 145 / 140 | trace amoun |
| mod. Meyer medium | 108 / 100 | | | |
| mp °C sample | 129 | 83 | 144 | 117 |
| authentic sample | — | 103-104 | 148.5-149 | — |
| Analysis analytical (C H N) | 69.1  9.3  13.3 | 70.1  9.6  13.4 | 69.4  9.4  13.8 | — |
| calculated (C H N) | 69.2  9.6  13.5 | 69.2  9.6  13.5 | 69.2  9.6  13.5 | |

it changed to a green-fluorescent compound with only slight mobility on thin-layer chromatography plates.

## Discussion

When industrial molds used in producing or found in Japanese foods were screened by examination of $R_f$ values and fluorescence spectra on thin-layer chromatograms, compounds resembling aflatoxin B were found to be produced by many strains. Compound B1 produced by each of these different molds resembles aflatoxin $B_1$ with respect to $R_f$ value on chromatograms developed with chloroform:methanol (98:2). However, other criteria such as ultraviolet absorption spectra, infrared absorption spectra, and others indicate that while the blue fluorescent compounds isolated are of similar chemical structure, they are different from aflatoxin $B_1$. The same can be said for compounds resembling aflatoxin G in chromatographic behavior. Therefore such methods are inadequate to establish unequivocally the production of afla-

Table 3. Characterization of compounds B4-B7 of
Aspergillus X-1.

| Sample | B4 | B5 | B6 | B7 |
|---|---|---|---|---|
| Assigned chemical structure | H₃C H N CH₂–CH CH₃ / H₉C₂–C–C O CH₃ / O N H / H (structure) | | H₃C H N CH₂–CH CH₃ / H₉C₂–C–C O CH₃ / O N H / H (structure) | |
| Name of compound | deoxy–hydroxy– aspergillic acid | ———— | deoxy–hydroxy–muta– aspergillic acid | ———— |
| Molecular formula | $C_{12}H_{20}O_2N_2$ | ———— | $C_{11}H_{18}O_2N_2$ | $C_{11}H_{18}O_2N_2$ |
| Yield, mg/L Czapek Dox medium | trace amount | ———— | ———— | ———— |
| mod. Meyer medium | 339 / 100 | 311/100 ( mix. of B5 and B6 ) | | 240 |
| mp °C sample | 107 | 153–154 | 133–134.5 | 158–159 |
| authentic sample | 105–106 | ———— | ———— | ———— |
| Analysis     C   H   N | C   H   N | | C   H   N | C   H   N |
| analytical | 64.4  8.9  12.4 | ———— | 62.9  8.3  13.1 | 62.9  8.6  13.0 |
| calculated | 64.3  8.9  12.5 | | 62.9  8.6  13.3 | 62.9  8.6  13.3 |

toxins by molds (C. W. Hesseltine, O. L. Shotwell, J. J. Ellis, and R. D. Stubbelfield, 1965, private communication; Aibara and Miyaki, 1965; Masuda et al., 1965).

The strains of Aspergillus tested are used by major Japanese fermentation food industries; therefore it can be said that fermented foods such as shoyu, miso, amasake, sake, and mirin are not contaminated with aflatoxins derived from the seed molds investigated.

Compound B2 was shown to be flavacol. Other aflatoxinlike compounds were related to each other, with a pyrazine ring common to their structures. This is indicated by similar ultraviolet spectra with absorption at 310 to 330 mμ, and infrared spectra with absorption at 1600 to 1700 cm$^{-1}$. Compounds B3, B5, and B7 are different from the other five B-compounds and presumably contain one -NH₂ radical indicated by strong infrared absorption at about 3400 cm$^{-1}$.

The compounds 2-hydroxy-3:6-di-sec-butylpyzine, flavacol, deoxyhydroxyaspergillic acid, in which the No. 1 position of py-

razine rings is =N-H, show fluorescence, while aspergillic acid
and hydroxyaspergillic acid, in which the same position is =N-OH,
show no fluorescence. This suggests that the deoxy structure is
required for these types of compounds to manifest the fluorescence
property. The high absorption peak in the infrared spectrum at
around 950 cm$^{-1}$ seems to be associated with these differences.
Fluorescent flavacol-series compounds display this characteristic,
whereas nonfluorescent aspergillic acid-series compounds do not.
This conclusion offers some suggestions for the chemical structures of unknown compounds B3, B5, B7, A2, and A3.

The occurrence of strains that produce aflatoxinlike compounds
was somewhat higher for the strains used for shoyu and miso than
those used for alcoholic beverages. The raw materials for shoyu
and miso contain a higher percentage of proteins, while those for
alcoholic beverages are rich in carbohydrate. The strains used
for shoyu and miso possess stronger protease than amylase, while
the opposite can be said for the strains for alcoholic beverages.
Compounds related to flavacol and aspergillic acid seem to be
formed together with active amino acid metabolism in strains used
for shoyu and miso. But there is not always correlation between
the production of these compounds and the presence of protease.
The strains of strong protease producers from prominent shoyu
manufacturers gave only trace amounts of aflatoxinlike fluorescent
spots and, at the same time, very small amounts of aspergillic
acid. As described in the introduction, koji cultured with Aspergillus X-1 (a nonindustrial strain that gives high yields of aflatoxinlike compounds and aspergillic acid) does not contain these compounds. It should be recognized, of course, that our data on production of aflatoxinlike compounds were not limited to Aspergillus
X-1, but also to production by strains actually used in preparation
of fermented foods.

## Conclusions

1. None of the 73 seed culture or starter strains of Aspergilli
tested under our conditions produced aflatoxins. These findings
confirm the reports of Hesseltine et al. (1965), Aibara and Miyake
(1965), and Masuda et al. (1965).

2. The strains tested produced compounds displaying $R_f$ values
and fluorescence data similar to aflatoxins under certain experimental conditions. However, isolation and characterization demonstrated that these compounds differ markedly in chemical structure
from aflatoxins.

3. In detection and characterization of samples suspected to be
contaminated with aflatoxins, $R_f$ values should be determined with
two or more solvent systems, and ultraviolet and infrared absorption spectral data should also be used. This implies that the compounds must be chemically isolated and identified.

4.  The possibility that koji cultures may become contaminated with aflatoxin-producing mold strains has been suggested.  This possibility does exist for fermented foods as it also does for most foods upon which molds grow.

5.  However, industrial seed cultures are heavily inoculated with enormous numbers of spores of non-aflatoxin-producing, starter strains.  This may account for our inability to detect aflatoxin in Japanese fermented food preparations including shoyu, miso, and sake.

## Acknowledgment

The authors would like to express their sincere appreciation to Dr. K. Sakaguchi and Dr. Y. Sumiki of Tokyo University, Dr. G. N. Wogan and Dr. R. I. Mateles of the Massachusetts Institute of Technology, Dr. C. W. Hesseltine of the Northern Regional Research Laboratory of the U.S. Department of Agriculture and Dr. H. Tsuchiya of Minnesota University, for their very kind interest in our research. They are also very grateful to Dr. K. Aibara of the National Institute of Health, Dr. S. Suzuki of the Institute of Physical and Chemical Research, and Dr. S. Nakamura of their laboratory, for their very kind advice, and to Mr. H. Homma of the Institute of Physical and Chemical Research, Mr. K. Hayashi and Mr. Y. Kaneko of their laboratory, for their valuable assistance.

## References

Aibara, K., and K. Miyaki, 1965, Paper presented at the Annual Meeting of the Agricultural Chemical Society of Japan, Tokyo (April).

Asao, T., G. Büchi, M. M. Abdel Kader, S. B. Chang, E. L. Wick, and G. N. Wogan, 1963, J. Amer. Chem. Soc., 85, 1706.

Asao, Y., and T. Yokotsuka, 1958, J. Agric. Chem. Soc. Japan., 32, 617.

Chang, S. B., M. M. Abdel Kader, E. L. Wick, and G. N. Wogan, 1963, Science, 142(3596), 1191.

Dunn, G., G. T. Newbold, and F. S. Spring, 1949, J. Chem. Soc., 2586.

Dutcher, J. D., 1957, J. Biol. Chem., 232, 785.

Hartley, R. D., B. F. Nesbitt, and J. O'Kelly, 1963, Nature (London), 198, 1056.

Kaneko, Y., 1965, Agric. Biol. Chem., 29, 965.

Kaneko, Y., M. Yamamoto, T. Mizutani, and S. Matsuura, 1966, Paper presented at the Annual Meeting of the Agricultural Chemical Society of Japan, Kyoto (April).

Kihara, Y., H. Murooka, and K. Sakaguchi, 1948, J. Ferm. Tech., 26, 297.

Masuda, Y., K. Mori, and M. Kuratsune (1965). Paper presented at the Annual Meeting of the Japanese Cancer Association, Fukuoka (October).

Murakami, H., Y. Ikeda, S. Hyodo, K. Oowaki, K. Kuwahara, and S. Takase, 1966, Paper presented at the Annual Meeting of the Agricultural Chemical Society of Japan, Tokyo (April).

Nakamura, S., and T. Shiro, 1959, Bull. Agric. Chem. Soc. Japan., 23, 418.

Nesbitt, B. F., J. O'Kelly, K. Sargeant, and A. Sheridan, 1962, Nature (London), 195, 1062.

Sakaguchi, K., and K. Yamada, 1944, J. Agric. Chem. Soc. Japan., 20, 65.

Takase, S., Y. Hukui, and H. Murakami, 1965, Paper presented at the Annual Meeting of the Society of Fermentation Technology of Japan, Osaka (November).

Thom, T., and M. B. Church, 1926, The Aspergilli, Williams and Wilkins Co., Baltimore, Maryland, p. 259.

# RECENT ADVANCES IN RESEARCH ON OCHRATOXIN

## Part 1

### Toxicological Aspects

I. F. H. Purchase and W. Nel
Division of Toxicology
National Nutrition Research Institute
Council for Scientific and Industrial Research
Pretoria, South Africa

In 1960 Dr. Isaacson, a pathologist at the Baragwanath Hospital in Johannesburg, was impressed with the work of Miyake and others in Japan on the carcinogenic effects of Penicillium islandicum (Isaacson, 1966). As a pathologist in a hospital serving a large population of Bantu in the Transvaal, he had noticed, as had many others before him, that the Bantu population of Southern Africa, as in many other parts of Africa, suffered from a very high incidence of liver cancer. This incidence was so high that in certain areas liver cancer was responsible for more deaths than any other cancer, and cases were frequently reported in teenagers and young children. All the theories of the causes of hepatoma (such as malnutrition, bilharziasis, siderosis, virus infection, and many others) have serious drawbacks for one reason or another; for example, malnutrition is common in Egypt, but hepatoma is not. The concept that mold metabolites can produce cancer and could be implicated in the causation of cancer in the Far East, immediately suggested that a similar etiological relationship in the case of Bantu hepatoma needed prompt investigation. The results from the initial studies that resulted from this suggestion have now been published. Scott (1965) reported the isolation of a number of strains of fungi from South African cereals and legume products and was able to show that 22 of these strains were toxic.

The investigation of the toxic principles and toxicity of some of these strains is now in progress, and, although we are a long way from showing any relationship between hepatoma and mycotoxins, some interesting new facts about mycotoxins have come to light.

One of the toxic strains of Aspergillus ochraceus was selected for investigation of the chemistry and toxicology of its metabolites.

In due course, a toxic substance was isolated from moldy cornmeal inoculated with <u>A. ochraceus</u>; this substance accounted for
most of the toxicity of the fungus. The toxic metabolite, called
ochratoxin, was shown to have the structures given in Figure 1
(Van der Merwe et al, 1965a). Two related substances, ochratoxin B and C (Figure 1), were also isolated, but have proved to
be much less active.

Fig. 1.   (a) R = H; R$^1$ = Cl: Ochratoxin A; (b) R = H; R$^1$ = H:
          Ochratoxin B; (c) R = CH$_2$CH$_3$; R$^1$ = Cl: Ochratoxin C.

We have chosen to study the toxicology of ochratoxin A because
it is a highly toxic metabolite and because of the presence of a
lactone grouping in its structure. The first task was to produce
a reasonable quantity of the toxin for biological work. The toxic
strain of <u>A. ochraceus</u> was grown on sterilized cornmeal and the
toxin quantitatively extracted with chloroform-methanol. The extract was concentrated, and the ochratoxin was extracted into sat-
urated sodium bicarbonate solution, which was then acidified with
hydrochloric acid. The ochratoxin was then extracted from the
acidified solution with chloroform and the extract purified on an
ion-exchange or formamide-impregnated cellulose column. Final
purification was obtained by recrystallization from benzene. The
final product, a white crystalline substance, contains one molecule of benzene of crystallization.

A similar extraction and cleanup procedure may be used for assaying for ochratoxin. Visualization of the toxin under ultraviolet
light after separation on silica thin-layer chromatoplates in a
methanol:benzene:acetic acid (45:8:4) mixture is relatively easy.
Quantitative estimation of the amount of ochratoxin may be ac-

complished by comparison with standard solutions on thin-layer
chromatoplates.  Although this technique has serious drawbacks,
it is the only procedure that has been developed so far.

The first biological studies of ochratoxin were histochemical
and electron microscopic studies of the effects on the livers of
day-old ducklings (Theron et al., 1965).  There was a mild fatty
infiltration of the hepatocytes, but no changes were observed in
the enzymes studied by histochemistry.  Electron-microscopic
studies revealed morphological changes in the mitochondria about
4 hours after dosing.  At first the mitochondria were swollen and
round, and later the matrix was coarsely granular, with compres-
sion of the cristae against the external membranes of the organelle.
Morphological changes in the endoplasmic reticulum also occurred.
Four hours after dosage, the endoplasmic reticulum was reduced
in amount and was exclusively present in the form of isolated dilated vesicles with focal loss of ribosomes from the ergastoplas-
mic membranes.  There was an increase in the numbers of free
ribosomes in the cytoplasm.  The process of dilation of the cis-
ternae eventually extended to the nuclear envelope.  At later stages
in the experiment, organelles were found free in the sinusoids, apparently after discharge through gaps in the sinusoidal endothelium.

The $LD_{50}$ values for day-old ducklings was stated to be about
25 µg (Van der Merwe et al., 1965b).  Our recent studies using a
statistical technique and larger numbers of ducklings have shown
that this figure is too low and that the true value is in the order of
150 µg per duckling.  The acute toxicity of ochratoxin has also
been studied in 150 g albino rats and was found to be approximately 20 mg/kg per os.

The rats used in the $LD_{50}$ estimations either died or were killed
at 10 days.  At autopsy the main macroscopic changes were enteritis (mainly of the small intestine), pale, enlarged liver, and
signs of degeneration and necrosis in the kidneys.  Histopatholog-
ical examination of paraffin-mounted sections of lung, liver, heart,
and kidney revealed the following lesions.  In the rats that died
within 2 days of oral dosage there was a single-cell necrosis of the
liver in some cases, but the main change was a tubular necrosis of
the kidney, which in the most severe cases appeared to affect the
majority of the cells in all the tubules.  The glomerular changes
were minimal.  In rats that died toward the termination of the experiment and in those that were killed at the end of the 10-day experimental period, there was a slight vacuolation of the liver.
The kidney lesions varied in intensity.  In some cases there was
a tubular necrosis affecting mainly the collecting tubules, and in
others there were no obvious abnormalities; the degree of change
depended on the dose of ochratoxin.  In several animals that were
killed 10 days after a low dose of ochratoxin, there was dilatation
of a wedge-shaped group of tubules in the cortex.  The dilated
tubules in some cases extended into the medulla, and in a few cases

the apex of the wedge pointed toward an area of round-cell infiltration in the outer zone of the medulla. Higher magnification of the tubules showed that the cellular lining was flattened and the nuclei unevenly distributed around the tubule. No clear intercellular membrane was visible between the cells of the dilated tubule. It is assumed that these tubules are dilated as a result of obstruction of a collecting tubule in the medulla with the result that, because the glomerulus was still functional, the nephron or nephrons affected became dilated.

Thus, ochratoxin A causes tubular necrosis of the kidney, mild degeneration of the liver, and enteritis.

A preliminary investigation into the metabolic fate of ochratoxin in rats has also been undertaken. Adult (200 g) rats were given an intraperitoneal injection of ochratoxin A (10 mg/kg) and the urine and feces collected for 72 hours. Extracts of both urine and feces were made and after purification were spotted on silica thin-layer chromatoplates, which were developed in benzene:acetic acid (8:2). Two fluorescent spots were seen and were identified as ochratoxin A and what appeared to be a degradation product of ochratoxin. Quantitative recoveries remain to be done, but it appears that ochratoxin A is excreted unchanged or as an isocoumarin derivative in the feces and urine in the first 48 to 72 hours. Ochratoxin A was also recovered from blood and liver, but only minute quantities of the isocoumarin derivative could be found. This derivative has subsequently been shown to be 3-methyl-5-chloro-8-hydroxy-dihydro-isocoumarin-7-carboxylic acid (see Figure 1).

This work will be extended in the near future, and studies of the subacute and chronic toxicity and the effects of ochratoxin on protein synthesis are planned. To this end, it is essential to have larger supplies of pure ochratoxin for these biological experiments. Therefore, the possibility of producing the toxin in liquid culture has been investigated. Work in this field forms the second part of this report.

# RECENT ADVANCES IN RESEARCH ON OCHRATOXIN

## Part 2

## Microbiological Aspects

### N. P. Ferreira*
Laboratorium voor Microbiologie
Technische Hogeschool, Delft, The Netherlands

Large quantities of ochratoxin are required for studies on the toxicological properties of the metabolite. Attempts to produce ochratoxin in submerged culture on conventional liquid media such as those of Czapek, Raulin-Thom, and the glucose-ammonium nitrate medium of Brian et al. (1961) were not successful. Further attempts were therefore made to produce ochratoxin in submerged culture.

## Materials and Methods

Organism. The organism used in the present investigation was a strain of Aspergillus ochraceus designated as strain K 804 in the culture collection of the Microbiology Research Group, Council for Scientific and Industrial Research, Pretoria. This strain was originally isolated from sorghum grain. The organism was maintained in sterile soil from which subcultures were made on Czapek agar, supplemented with 1% corn-steep liquor, for the preparation of spore suspensions. One ml of a freshly prepared and standardized spore suspension was used to inoculate the substrate in each flask.

Medium. The basal medium employed had the following composition: $KH_2PO_4$ 1.0 g; KCl 0.5 g; $MgSO_4 \cdot 7H_2O$ 0.5 g; distilled water 1 liter. Sucrose, 30 g/liter, was added as the carbon and energy source. Trace elements were added in the following concentrations in mg/liter: $FeCl_3 \cdot 6H_2O$ 24.2; $ZnSO_4 \cdot 7H_2O$ 21.99; $MnSO_4 \cdot 5H_2O$ 10.98; $CuSO_4 \cdot 5H_2O$ 3.93; and $(NH_4)_6MO_7O_{24} \cdot 4H_2O$ 2.52. Changes that were made in the composition of the medium

---

*Permanent address: Microbiology Research Group, South African Council for Scientific and Industrial Research, Pretoria, South Africa.

for individual experiments as well as the nitrogen source will be considered in the appropriate text. The pH was adjusted to 6.0 to 6.2 with KOH. The medium was sterilized at 10 lb per square inch for 15 minutes.

Cultural conditions. The fungus was cultured in 500 ml Erlenmeyer flasks (Pyrex) with one indentation as baffle. Each flask contained 100 ml of medium and was incubated on a rotary shaker at 250 rpm at 25°C for 6 days. No antifoam agent was added to the substrate because it was found that the omission of such an agent substantially reduced mycelial growth on the walls of the flasks.

Experiments carried out after the development of a medium suitable for the production of ochratoxin were conducted in 100 ml flat-bottomed flasks (Jena) and in 10 liter Marubishi fermentors. The 100 ml flasks contained 25 ml of medium and were incubated under the same conditions as the 500 ml flasks. Experiments in the fermentors were performed with 5.5 liters of medium at 25°C. This was agitated at a rate of 300 rpm and aerated with 3 to 4 liters of air per minute. All media were sterilized at 15 lb per square inch for 15 minutes.

Isolation and assay of ochratoxin. Ochratoxin was extracted from the acidified culture filtrate with chloroform in a liquid-liquid extractor. The metabolite was obtained from the mycelium by homogenizing this in a Waring blendor with a mixture of chloroform and methanol (1:1) for 2 minutes and repeating the extraction with chloroform for 1 minute. The concentration of ochratoxin present in the extracts was then estimated by thin-layer chromatography on silica-gel plates according to Steyn and van der Merve (1966). In ultraviolet light, ochratoxin appears as a yellow-green fluorescent spot on the plates. The concentration of ochratoxin in the extract was semiquantitatively determined by visually comparing the intensity of the fluorescent spot with the intensity of the fluorescence of a standard spot. Furthermore, the presence of ochratoxin in the extracts was confirmed by mass spectrometry.

Other analytical methods. Cell dry weight was determined by weighing the mycelium contained in an aliquot of the culture medium after it was dried overnight at 105°C; pH was measured electrometrically. Residual sugar was determined by the phenol-sulfuric acid method according to Hodge and Hofreiter (1962). Total nitrogen in the culture filtrate was estimated by means of the Kjeldahl method as described by Koch and Hanke (1948).

## Results

The investigation has led to the formulation of a medium that is suitable for the production of ochratoxin in submerged culture in fairly great amounts.

The results of the experiments in which various nitrogenous compounds were tested as sole sources of nitrogen are summarized in Table 1. All compounds examined supported mycelial

Table 1. Effect of Nitrogen Source on Production of Ochratoxin

| Nitrogen Source | Concentration g/liter | Final pH | Ochratoxin mg/liter |
|---|---|---|---|
| NaNO₃ | 2.0 | 7.0 | 0 |
| NH₄NO₃ | 2.0 | 7.9 | 2.5 |
| (NH₄)₂SO₄ | 2.0 | | 0 |
| NH₄Cl | 2.0 | | 0 |
| Ammonium acetate | 10.0 | 7.5 | 50.0 |
| | 5.0 | 6.0 | 0 |
| Corn-steep liquor | 10.0 | 6.7 | 10.0 |
| | 5.0 | 6.4 | 0 |
| Casamino acids | 15.0 | 7.1 | 10.0 |
| | 7.5 | 6.4 | 2.0 |
| Asparagine | 5.0 | 5.8 | 2.0 |
| Aspartic acid | 10.0 | 8.4 | 5.0 |
| Glutamic acid | 10.0 | 8.0 | 100.0 |
| Proline | 8.0 | 6.6 | 100.0 |
| Leucine | 4.0 | 4.4 | 0 |
| Glycine | 3.0 | 5.6 | 2.0 |
| Phenylalanine | 12.0 | 4.6 | 0 |
| Arginine | 4.0 | 3.1 | 0 |

growth. The highest yields of ochratoxin were obtained in media containing glutamic acid or proline as sole nitrogen source. Lower yields were observed in culture filtrates to which ammonium acetate, corn-steep liquor, or casamino acids had been added as nitrogen source. The results listed in Table 2 indicate that a maximal yield of ochratoxin is obtained in presence of about 1% glutamic acid.

The production of ochratoxin in media that contained ammonium acetate or casamino acids as nitrogen source could be increased

Table 2.   Effect of Varying Concentrations of Glutamic Acid
on Ochratoxin Production

| Glutamic Acid g/liter | Final pH | Ochratoxin mg/liter |
|---|---|---|
| 2.5 | 6.8 | 2.0 |
| 5.0 | 7.3 | 50.0 |
| 7.5 | 7.8 | 100.0 |
| 10.0 | 8.0 | 100.0 |
| 15.0 | 8.0 | 100.0 |

by incorporating 0.25% lactic acid into the medium.   The addition of this acid did not affect the yield in media that contained glutamic acid as sole nitrogen source (see Table 3).

Table 3.   Effect of Lactic Acid (0.25%) on Ochratoxin
Production

| Nitrogen Source | Lactic Acid 0.25% | Final pH | Ochratoxin mg/liter |
|---|---|---|---|
| 1% Ammonium acetate | with | 8.5 | 100.0 |
|  | without | 7.5 | 50.0 |
| 1% Casamino acids | with | 7.7 | 50.0 |
|  | without | 7.1 | 10.0 |
| 1% Glutamic acid | with | 7.8 | 100.0 |
|  | without | 7.8 | 100.0 |

Table 4 gives the results of some experiments in which the sucrose of the basal medium was replaced by other compounds as carbon and energy source.  Glutamic acid at a concentration of 1% was added as the sole nitrogen source in all these experiments.  Heat-sensitive sugars were filter sterilized.  All carbon sources tested supported mycelial growth.  The preferred carbon source for ochratoxin production is sucrose.  Good yields of ochratoxin could also be obtained in cultures containing galactose as sole carbon source.  The results in Table 5 indicate that a concentration of 3% sucrose lies within the optimal range.

Experiments in shake flasks have proved that the concentration of the other constituents of the medium did not affect the yield of ochratoxin under the experimental conditions applied.

In view of the close relationship between glutamic acid and the intermediates of the tricarboxylic acid cycle, the effect of other constituents of this cycle on the production of ochratoxin was in-

Table 4.   Effect of Carbon Source on the Production of
           Ochratoxin

| Carbon Source | Concentration g/liter | Final pH | Ochratoxin mg/liter |
|---|---|---|---|
| Sucrose | 30.0 | 8.0 | 100.0 |
| Glucose | 30.0 | 8.0 | 2.0 |
| Fructose | 30.0 | 7.8 | 0 |
| Galactose | 30.0 | 7.4 | 75.0 |
| Maltose | 30.0 | 6.5 | 2.0 |
| Lactose | 30.0 | 7.8 | 0 |
| Mannitol | 30.0 | 6.5 | 0 |
| Glycerol | 30.0 | 6.3 | 0 |
| Lactose + Sucrose | 20 + 10 | 7.8 | 100.0 |
| Lactose + Sucrose | 15 + 15 | 8.0 | 100.0 |
| Lactose + Sucrose | 10 + 20 | 7.8 | 100.0 |
| Glucose + Fructose | 20 + 10 | 7.8 | 2.0 |
| Glucose + Fructose | 15 + 15 | 7.8 | 2.0 |
| Glucose + Fructose | 10 + 20 | 7.8 | 2.0 |
| Glutamic acid | 15.0 | 7.2 | 0 |

Table 5.   Effect of Various Concentrations of Sucrose on
           Ochratoxin Production

| Sucrose g/liter | Final pH | Ochratoxin mg/liter |
|---|---|---|
| 10 | 7.4 | 40.0 |
| 15 | 7.4 | 100.0 |
| 30 | 7.8 | 100.0 |
| 45 | 7.8 | 100.0 |
| 60 | 8.0 | 100.0 |

vestigated. In these experiments, the compounds were added to
the basal medium, which contained 0.2% ammonium nitrate as
nitrogen source, in concentrations of 0.05 and 0.2%. No marked
stimulation of ochratoxin production occurred except in the case
of glutamic acid itself.

The effect of glutamic acid was investigated further by supplementing the ammonium nitrate medium with different concentrations of glutamic acid after incubation periods of varying duration. Glutamic acid was added to the medium in concentrations of 0.05 and 0.2% at zero time and after 24, 48, and 72 hours, respectively. All cultures were harvested after an incubation period of 6 days. The stimulatory effect of glutamic acid on the production of ochratoxin diminished as the time interval preceding the addition of the amino acid increased (see Table 6).

Table 6.  Effect of Addition of Glutamic Acid on Production of Ochratoxin in Nonproducing Media

| Age of Culture hours | Glutamic Acid Added g/liter | Final pH | Ochratoxin mg/liter |
|---|---|---|---|
| 0 | 0.5 | 6.0 | 100.0 |
| 24 | 0.5 | 5.6 | 100.0 |
| 48 | 0.5 | 5.6 | 50.0 |
| 72 | 0.5 | 6.2 | 2.0 |
| 0 | 2.0 | 6.0 | 100.0 |
| 24 | 2.0 | 6.4 | 100.0 |
| 48 | 2.0 | 6.6 | 50.0 |
| 72 | 2.0 | 6.6 | 2.0 |
| Control | - | 6.0 | 5.0 |

Experiments were conducted subsequently in which the production of ochratoxin was studied in relation to incubation time and substrate utilization. The course of a fermentation, which was carried out in 100 ml flasks with 1% glutamic acid as nitrogen source, is shown in Figure 2. The data given represent the average values obtained from triplicate cultures that were analyzed individually.

The ochratoxin fermentation can clearly be divided into three phases.

The first phase is characterized by a relatively slow utilization of substrate and a correspondingly slow increase in mycelial dry weight. The pH rises during this phase, and no ochratoxin can be detected in the culture filtrate or mycelium.

The second phase is characterized by a rapid increase in mycelial dry weight and a concomitant increase in the rate of substrate utilization. The pH remains constant initially but eventually rises in the later stages of the phase. This phase is further characterized by the appearence of ochratoxin in the culture fil-

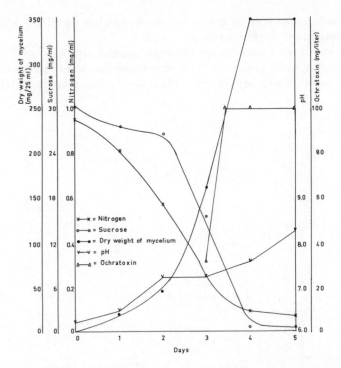

Fig. 2.  Results of fermentation in 100 ml flat-bottomed
flasks in basal medium plus 3% sucrose and 1%
glutamic acid.

trate and mycelium, ochratoxin A being formed simultaneously
with the components B and C.  The production of these metabolites is completed in a period of 12 to 24 hours, after which the
concentration remains constant.  In a separate experiment it was
found that the concentration was constant over a period of 15 days
subsequent to the appearence of the metabolites in the culture filtrate.

In the final stage, characterized by a constant concentration of
ochratoxin, the dry weight of the mycelium at first remains constant and then decreases.  This phase has, however, not yet been
investigated in detail.

In another series of experiments, the production of ochratoxin
was investigated at various concentrations of sucrose and glutamic
acid at a constant C:N ratio.  The experiments were carried out
at sucrose concentrations of 6, 3, and 1.5% and glutamic acid concentrations of 2, 1, and 0.5%, respectively.

These experiments were performed in the Marubishi fermentors.  Each fermentor was inoculated with 5% inoculum.  This was
prepared by preculturing the fungus in 500 ml flasks at 25°C on a
rotary shaker for 36 hours.  The medium used for the preparation

of the inoculum was of the same composition as that employed in the subsequent fermentation.

The results of these experiments appear in Figures 3 through 6. It is evident that the course of fermentation at all three C:N ratios is essentially the same. Moreover, the course is similar to

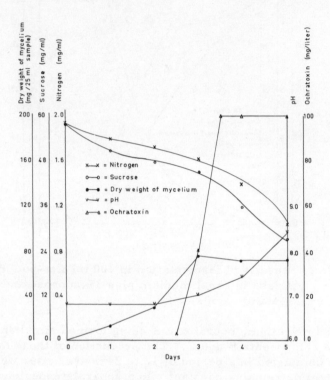

Fig. 3.   Results of fermentation in the Marubishi fermentor in basal medium plus 1.5% sucrose and 0.5% glutamic acid.

that recorded in the shake cultures in 100 ml flasks. Qualitative differences may, however, be discerned in the relation between the amount of substrate consumed and the quantity of ochratoxin produced.

An experiment was also conducted on the pilot plant scale in 100 liter medium containing 3% sucrose and 1% glutamic acid. The course of the fermentation observed in this experiment was again similar to that found in other cultures. However, the yield of ochratoxin was lower than that obtained in shake-flasks and in the Marubishi fermentors at the same concentration of sucrose and amino acid. It amounted to approximately 50 mg per liter.

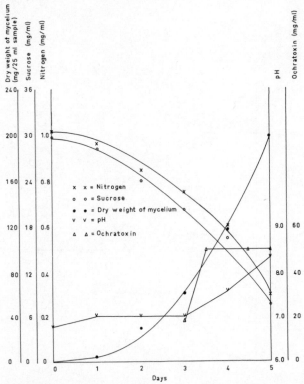

Fig. 4.  Results of fermentation in the Marubishi fermentor in
basal medium plus 3% sucrose and 1% glutamic acid.

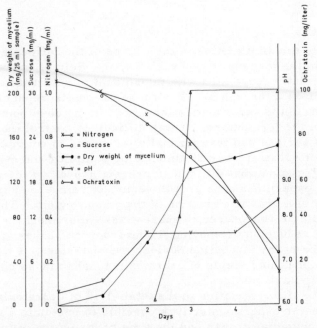

Fig. 5.  Results of fermentation in the Marubishi fermentor in
basal medium plus 3% sucrose and 1% glutamic acid.

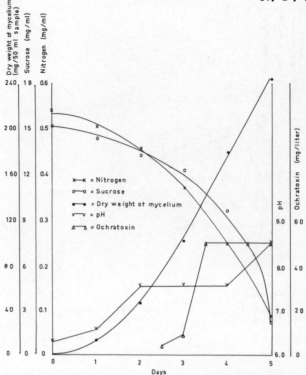

Fig. 6.  Results of fermentation in the Marubishi fermentor in
basal medium plus 6% sucrose and 2% glutamic acid.

## Discussion

Despite the similarities in the course of the fermentations observed in the fermentor experiments, the yield of ochratoxin cannot be strictly correlated with the amount of substrate supplied
(cf. Figures 2 through 6).  The cause of the discrepancies must
be sought in the variation that occurred in the development of the
fungus in the fermentors.  It was difficult to control the formation of a surface pad that gradually increased in volume as the
volume of substrate was diminished by sampling and evaporation;
it was also somewhat difficult to prevent growth on the sparger.
In some experiments the growth seriously hampered aeration and
resulted in a drastic reduction of the product yield.  This phenomenon could be reproduced in shake-flask experiments in which aeration was reduced by removing flasks from the shaker at intervals
during the 6-day incubation period.  Nevertheless, it was possible
to obtain maximal yields of ochratoxin equal to those observed in
the shake-flask cultures.

In spite of the variation in the total yield of ochratoxin observed
in fermentor experiments, it is possible to postulate a correlation
between mycelial growth and the time of formation of this metabo-

lite.  Ochratoxin appeared in all fermentations when the growth
had reached the logarithmic phase as measured by dry weight of
mycelium and substrate utilization.  This is in contrast with many
other fermentations in which secondary metabolites are produced
after growth has almost ceased.

No explanation can be given at present for the narrow range of
substrates on which the fungus produces ochratoxin.  The apparent absolute requirement for sucrose appears all the more strange
as very little ochratoxin is produced in media that contain mixtures
of fructose and glucose in different ratios or one of these sugars
singly.  It is of interest to note that the only other nitrogen source
that is as efficient as glutamic acid (viz., proline) is generally
transformed to glutamate before being metabolized (Nicholas,
1965).

## Summary

The production of ochratoxin A by a strain of Aspergillus ochraceus was studied in shake-flasks and in 10 liter Marubishi fermentors.  These studies have led to the formulation of a synthetic
medium that is suitable for the production of the metabolite
mentioned in fairly great amounts.  The carbon and nitrogen
sources of choice are sucrose and glutamate, respectively.

The effect of various concentrations of sucrose and glutamate
on the production of ochratoxin was investigated.  These experiments were conducted in the Marubishi fermentors at a constant
C:N ratio.  In addition, the production of the metabolite was examined in relation to substrate utilization and time.  It appeared
that the toxin is produced in the early stages of the logarithmic
phase of growth.

The concentration of ochratoxin in the extracts obtained from
the culture filtrates was estimated by means of thin-layer chromatography on silica-gel plates.

The maximal yield observed in shake-flasks and that found in
10 liter fermentations did not differ significantly and amounted
to approximately 100 mg per liter of medium.

The substrate used in the above experiments has also been applied in pilot plant fermentations with 100 liters of medium.  The
yield of ochratoxin A observed so far under these conditions was
approximately 50 mg per liter.

## References

Brian, P. W., A. W. Dawkins, J. F. Grove, H. G. Hemming,
    D. Lowe, and G. L. F. Norris, 1961, J. Exptl. Botany, 12, 1.

Hodge, J. E., and B. Hofreiter, 1962, in Methods in Carbohydrate
    Chemistry, Vol. 1, Academic Press, New York, p. 389.

Isaacson, C., 1966, South African Medical Journal, 40, 11.

Koch, F. C., and M. E. Hanke, 1948, Practical Methods in Biochemistry, 5th Ed., The Williams & Wilkins Co., Baltimore, Maryland, p. 176.

Nicholas, D. J. D., 1965, in The Fungi, Vol. 1, Academic Press, New York, p. 349.

Scott, De B., 1965, Mycopathol. Mycol. Appl., 25, 213.

Steyn, P. S., and K. J. van der Merwe, 1966. Nature, 211, 418.

Theron, J. J., N. Liebenberg, and H. J. B. Joubert, 1965, S. African Med. J., 39, 767.

van der Merwe, K. J., P. S. Steyn, and L. Fourie, 1965a, J. Chem. Soc., 7083.

van der Merwe, K. J., P. S. Steyn, L. Fourie, De B. Scott, and J. J. Theron, 1965b, Nature, 205, 1112.

# INDEX